# OBART INSTITUTE
## OF WELDING TECHNOLOGY

# Pocket Welding Guide
## A Guide to Better Welding
### 32nd Edition

Filler metal information courtesy
Hobart Brothers Company, Troy, Ohio, US

State Board of Career Colleges and Schools
Registration No. 70-12-0064HT

Accrediting Commission of Career Schools
and Colleges of Technology No. 000403

ISBN: 978-1-936058-28-0

# FOREWORD

This 32nd edition of the *Pocket Welding Guide* is dedicated to all those who are interested in and work with any aspect of welding. It covers a wide variety of subjects that are essential for the student or beginner and are of interest to the veteran welders, draftsmen, instructors, supervisors, foremen, technicians, and engineers.

You are encouraged to *strive for the perfect weld*. Putting every effort forth to attain it will make you more valuable as a welder. No matter what your task may be, you can do no better than to try for perfection.

# INTRODUCTION

The *Pocket Welding Guide* began as a 30-page booklet with 3.5 x 5.5-inch dimensions that would actually fit into a shirt pocket. In fact, the early title of the book was *Hobart Vest Pocket Guide to Better Welding*.

The booklet contained three types of electrodes, four essentials of proper welding procedures, types of joints and welding positions, early welding symbols, some of the early *build your own* Hobart welding generators, and a page of the early "Practical Arc Welding" training books.

The "up-to-date welding training" was, at that time, being provided at the Hobart Trade School. It is stated on the cover, "Thousands of men and women have received thorough training at the Hobart Trade School, and have immediately stepped into high paying jobs."

It goes on to indicate that the training was being offered "to those interested in preparing for steady employment in post-war industry." And that training was "fully accredited under the G.I. Bill."

With each new edition, more information was added. More welding symbols were developed, welding terms have been standardized and added and today, in its 32nd edition, the book is 156 pages in length. The *Pocket Welding Guide* is a great addition to any welder's toolbox. It remains a quick and ready reference.

# Contents

# Welding & Cutting Processes

## SMAW

Shielded Metal Arc Welding, also called Stick welding and Manual Metal welding is an arc welding process with an arc between a covered electrode and the weld pool. Shielding is obtained from decomposition of the electrode covering. The process is normally manually applied and is capable of welding thin and thick steels and some nonferrous metals in all positions. The process requires a relatively high degree of welder skill.

## GMAW

Gas Metal Arc Welding, also known as MIG welding, $CO_2$ Welding, Micro Wire Welding, short arc welding, dip transfer welding, wire welding, etc., is an arc welding process using an arc between a continuous filler metal electrode and the weld pool. Shielding is obtained from an externally supplied gas or gas mixture. The process is normally applied semiautomatically; however, the process may be operated automatically and can be machine operated. The process can be used to weld thin and fairly thick steels and some nonferrous metals in all positions. A relatively low degree of welding skill is required for the process.

## FCAW

Flux Cored Arc Welding, also known as Dual-Shielded, Inner-shield, Self Shield, FabCO, etc., is an arc welding process using an arc between a continuous filler metal electrode and the weld pool. Shielding is obtained through decomposition of the flux within the tubular wire. Additional shielding may or may not be obtained from an externally supplied gas or gas mixture. The process is normally applied semi-automatically, but can be applied automatically or mechanized. It is commonly used to weld medium to thick steels using large diameter electrodes in the flat and horizontal position and small electrode diameters in all positions. The process is used to a lesser degree for welding stainless steel and for overlay work. The skill level required for FCAW is similar to GMAW.

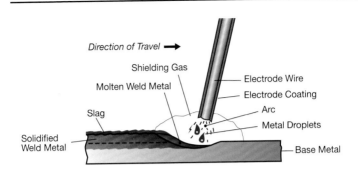

Direction of Travel ➡

Shielding Gas

Molten Weld Metal

Slag

Solidified
Weld Metal

Electrode Wire

Electrode Coating

Arc

Metal Droplets

Base Metal

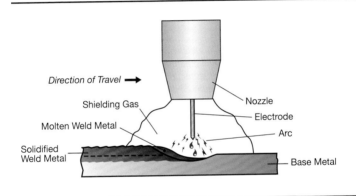

Direction of Travel ➡

Shielding Gas

Molten Weld Metal

Solidified
Weld Metal

Nozzle

Electrode

Arc

Base Metal

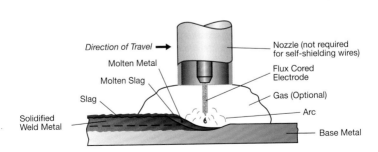

Direction of Travel ➡

Molten Metal

Molten Slag

Slag

Solidified
Weld Metal

Nozzle (not required
for self-shielding wires)

Flux Cored
Electrode

Gas (Optional)

Arc

Base Metal

# Welding & Cutting Processes

## SAW

Submerged Arc Welding, also known as Union Melt, Hidden Arc, Welding Under Powder, etc., is an arc welding process using an arc or arcs between a bare metal electrode or electrodes and the weld pool. The arc and molten metal are shielded by a blanket of granular flux on the workpieces. The process is normally applied mechanized or automatically, but is used on a limited basis semi-automatically. It is used to weld medium to thick steel in the flat and horizontal position only. Manual welding skill is not required; however, a technical understanding of the equipment and welding procedures is necessary to operate the process.

## GTAW

Gas Tungsten Arc Welding, also known as TIG welding, Heliarc Welding, Heli-Welding, Argon-Arc Welding and Tungsten Arc Welding, is an arc welding process using an arc between a tungsten electrode (nonconsumable) and the weld pool. Filler may or may not be used. Shielding is obtained from an inert gas or an inert gas mixture. The process is normally applied manually and is capable of welding steels and nonferrous metals in all positions. The process is commonly used on thin metals and for the root and hot pass on tubing and pipe. Requires a relatively high degree of welder skill.

## PAW

Plasma Arc Welding, sometimes referred to as Needle Arc and Micro Plasma, is an arc welding process employing a constricted arc between a nonconsumable electrode and the weld pool (transferred arc) or between the electrode and the constricting nozzle (nontransferred arc). Shielding is obtained from the hot ionized gas issuing from the orifice. An auxiliary inert shielding gas or mixture of inert gases may supplement the system. The process is commonly applied manually, but may be automatic to increase welding speeds. It can be used to weld almost all metals and can be all position at lower currents. Normally used on thinner metals, the process requires a slightly lesser degree of welder skill than Gas Tungsten Arc Welding, but a greater knowledge of equipment set-up.

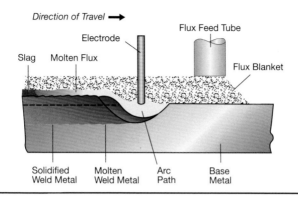

Direction of Travel →

Electrode
Flux Feed Tube
Slag
Molten Flux
Flux Blanket
Solidified Weld Metal
Molten Weld Metal
Arc Path
Base Metal

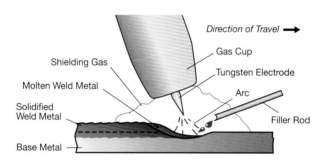

Direction of Travel →

Shielding Gas
Gas Cup
Tungsten Electrode
Molten Weld Metal
Arc
Filler Rod
Solidified Weld Metal
Base Metal

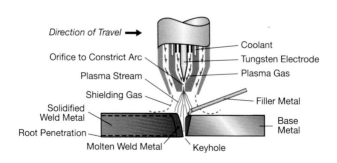

Direction of Travel →

Orifice to Constrict Arc
Coolant
Plasma Stream
Tungsten Electrode
Shielding Gas
Plasma Gas
Solidified Weld Metal
Filler Metal
Root Penetration
Base Metal
Molten Weld Metal
Keyhole

9

# Welding & Cutting Processes

## ESW

Electroslag Welding, also known as Porta-Slag or Slag Welding, is a welding process producing coalescence of metals with molten slag, melting the filler metal and the surfaces of the workpieces. The molten weld pool is shielded by a slag covering which moves along the joint as welding progresses. The process is not an arc welding process, except that an arc is used to start the process. After stabilization the molten slag provides the necessary heat for welding. The process is always applied automatically. It is a limited application process used only for making vertical welds on medium to heavy thickness of mild steel. Manual welding skill is not required, but a technical knowledge of the process is required to operate the equipment.

## SW

Stud Welding, also known as Arc Stud Welding, is an arc welding process using an arc between a metal stud, or similar part, and the other workpiece. Partial shielding is obtained by a ceramic ferrule surrounding the stud. It is a mechanized welding process, using a specialized gun that holds the stud and makes the weld. The process is normally used on steels in the flat and horizontal position. A low degree of welding skill is required for stud welding operation.

## OAW

Oxyacetylene Welding, sometimes referred to as Gas Welding, Oxy-Fuel Gas Welding, and Torch Welding, is an oxyfuel gas welding process employing acetylene as the fuel gas. The process may be used with or without filler metal. It can be used on thin to medium thickness metals of many types, steels and nonferrous in all positions. The process is applied manually and requires a relatively high degree of welding skill.

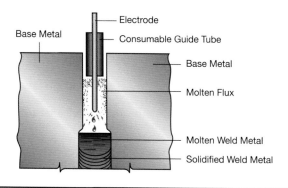

- Base Metal
- Electrode
- Consumable Guide Tube
- Base Metal
- Molten Flux
- Molten Weld Metal
- Solidified Weld Metal

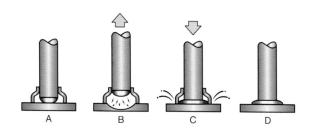

A    B    C    D

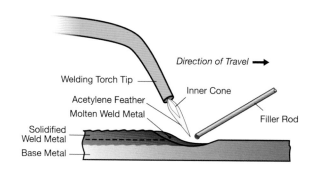

- Direction of Travel →
- Welding Torch Tip
- Inner Cone
- Acetylene Feather
- Molten Weld Metal
- Filler Rod
- Solidified Weld Metal
- Base Metal

## TB

Torch Brazing, sometimes called Gas Brazing, is similar to Oxyacetylene Welding, except the base metal is not melted, and the filler metal is usually a nonferrous metal. The filler metal flows into the joint by capillary action. Brazing can be done in all positions on most metals and is especially popular for repair work on case iron. The process is normally applied manually and requires a relatively high degree of brazer skill.

## OC

Oxygen Cutting, also known as Oxygen Fuel Gas Cutting, Acetylene Cutting, Gas Cutting and Burning, is a thermal process used to sever metals by heating the metal with a flame to an elevated temperature and using pure oxygen to oxidize the metal and produce the cut. Different fuel gases can be used including: acetylene, natural gas, propane and various trade-name gases. The process is normally applied manually with hand-held torches or mechanized with highly accurate tracing devices and multi-torches for cutting simultaneous shapes. It is used to cut thin to very thick metals, primarily steels; however, with various arrangements it can be used on other metals. Manual oxygen cutting requires a fairly high degree of flamecutter skill.

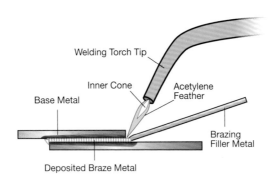

Welding Torch Tip

Inner Cone

Acetylene Feather

Base Metal

Brazing Filler Metal

Deposited Braze Metal

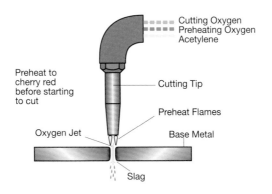

Cutting Oxygen
Preheating Oxygen
Acetylene

Preheat to cherry red before starting to cut

Cutting Tip

Preheat Flames

Oxygen Jet

Base Metal

Slag

# Welding & Cutting Processes

## PAC

Plasma Arc Cutting, sometimes called Plasma Burning and Plasma Machining, is an arc cutting process which severs metal by melting a localized area with a constricted arc and removing the molten material with a high velocity jet of hot ionized gas issuing from the orifice. It can be used with a hand held torch manually or mechanized cutting in extremely accurate machines with special tracing devices. It is used for cutting steels and non ferrous metals in thin to medium thicknesses. The process requires a lesser degree of cutter skill than oxygen cutting except the equipment is much more complex for manual operation.

## CAC-A

Air Carbon Arc Gouging is a process in which metals to be cut are melted by the heat of a carbon arc and the molten metal is removed by a blast of air. Normally, it is a manual operation used in all positions, but may also be operated automatically. The process can be used on steels and some nonferrous metals. The process is commonly used for back gouging welds, for gouging out defective welds and repairing castings. The process requires a relatively high degree of cutting skills.

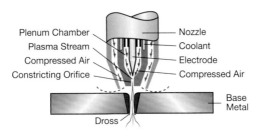

Plenum Chamber — Nozzle
Plasma Stream — Coolant
Compressed Air — Electrode
Constricting Orifice — Compressed Air
Base Metal
Dross

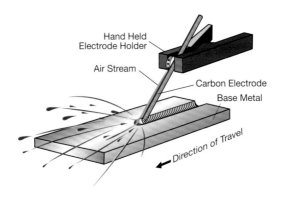

Hand Held Electrode Holder
Air Stream
Carbon Electrode
Base Metal
Direction of Travel

# 5 Essentials for Good Welding

1. **Correct Electrode Size**
2. **Correct Current**
3. **Correct Arc Length**
4. **Correct Travel Speed**
5. **Correct Electrode Angle**

Besides the steady sizzling sound that a correct arc produces, the shape of the molten pool and the movement of the metal at the rear of the pool serve as a guide in checking weld quality. In a correctly made deposit the ripples produced on the bead will be uniform and the bead will be smooth, with no overlap or undercut.

### 1. Correct Electrode Size

The correct choice of electrode size involves consideration of a variety of factors, such as the type, position, and preparation of the joint, the ability of the electrode to carry high current values without injury to the weld metal or loss of deposition efficiency, the mass of work metal and its ability to maintain its original properties after welding, the characteristics of the assembly with reference to effect of stresses set up by heat application, the practicability of heat treatment before and/or after welding, the specific requirements as to welding quality and the cost of achieving the desired results.

### 2. Correct Current

If current on equipment is too high or too low, you are certain to be disappointed in your weld. If too high, the electrode melts too fast and your molten pool is large and irregular. If too low, there is not enough heat to melt the base metal and your molten pool will be too small, will pile up, look irregular.

### 3. Correct Arc Length

If the arc is too long or voltage too high the metal melts off the electrode in large globules which wobble from side to side as the arc wavers, giving a wide, spattered and irregular bead — with poor fusion between original metal and deposited metal. If the arc is too short, or voltage too low, there is not enough heat to melt the base metal properly and the electrode quite often sticks to the work, giving a high, uneven bead, having irregular ripples with poor fusion.

### 4. Correct Travel Speed

When your speed is too fast your pool does not last long enough, impurities and gas are locked in. The bead is narrow and ripples pointed. When speed is too slow the metal piles up, the bead is high and wide, with a rather straight ripple.

### 5. Correct Electrode Angle

The electrode angle is of particular importance in fillet welding and deep groove welding. Generally speaking, when making a fillet weld, the electrode should be held so that it bisects the angle between the plates (as shown at right) and is perpendicular to the line of weld. If undercut occurs in the vertical member, lower the angle of the arc and direct the arc toward the vertical member.

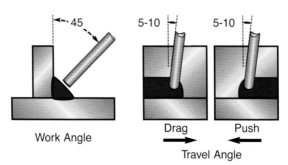

Work Angle

Drag     Push

Travel Angle

# Examples of Good & Bad Welds
## – Shielded Metal Arc Welding

| GOOD<br>Proper Current<br>Voltage & Speed | BAD<br>Welding Current<br>Too Low | BAD<br>Welding Current<br>Too High |
|---|---|---|
|  |  |  |
| Cross-section Weld Bead | Cross-section Weld Bead | Cross-section Weld Bead |
|  |  |  |
| Face Weld Bead | Face Weld Bead | Face Weld Bead |
| A smooth, regular, well formed bead.<br><br>No undercutting, overlapping or piling up.<br><br>Uniform in cross section.<br><br>Excellent weld at minimal material and labor cost. | Excessive piling up of weld metal.<br><br>Overlapping bead has poor penetration.<br><br>Slow up progress.<br><br>Wasted electrodes and productive time. | Excessive spatter to be cleaned off.<br><br>Undercutting along edges weakens joint.<br><br>Irregular deposit.<br><br>Wasted electrodes and productive time. |

# Examples of Good & Bad Welds
## – Shielded Metal Arc Welding

| **BAD**<br>**Arc Too Long**<br>**(Voltage Too High)** | **BAD**<br>**Welding Speed**<br>**Too Fast** | **BAD**<br>**Welding Speed**<br>**Too Slow** |
|---|---|---|
|  |  |  |
| Cross-section Weld Bead | Cross-section Weld Bead | Cross-section Weld Bead |
|  |  |  |
| Face Weld Bead | Face Weld Bead | Face Weld Bead |
| Bead very irregular with poor penetration. | Bead too small, with contour irregular. | Excessive piling up of weld metal. |
| Weld metal not properly shielded. | Not enough weld metal in cross section. | Overlapping without penetration at edges. |
| An inefficient weld. | Weld not strong enough. | Too much time consumed. |
| Wasted electrodes and productive time. | Wasted electrodes and productive time. | Wasted electrodes and productive time. |

# Examples of Good & Bad Welds
## – Flux Cored without External Shielding Gas

| GOOD<br>Proper Current<br>Voltage & Speed | BAD<br>Welding Current<br>Too Low<br>(High Voltage) | BAD<br>Welding Current<br>Too High<br>(Low Voltage) |
|---|---|---|
| <br>Cross-section Fillet | <br>Cross-section Fillet | <br>Cross-section Fillet |
| <br>Cross-section Weld Bead | <br>Cross-section Weld Bead | <br>Cross-section Weld Bead |
| 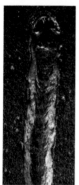<br>Face Weld Bead | 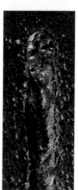<br>Face Weld Bead | <br>Face Weld Bead |
| A smooth, regular, well formed bead.<br><br>No undercutting, overlapping or piling up.<br><br>Uniform in cross section.<br><br>Excellent weld at minimal material and labor cost. | Excessive spatter and porosity.<br><br>Weld bead excessively wide and flat.<br><br>Undercutting along edges weakens joint.<br><br>Irregular bead contour. | Weld bead excessively convex and narrow.<br><br>Difficult slag removal.<br><br>Wasted filler metal and productive time. |

# Examples of Good & Bad Welds
## – Flux Cored without External Shielding Gas

| **BAD**<br>**Welding Speed**<br>**Too Fast** | **BAD**<br>**Welding Speed**<br>**Too Slow** | **BAD**<br>**Insufficient**<br>**Shielding Gas Coverage** |
|---|---|---|
| <br>Cross-section Fillet | <br>Cross-section Fillet | <br>Cross-section Fillet |
| <br>Cross-section Weld Bead | <br>Cross-section Weld Bead | <br>Cross-section Weld Bead |
| <br>Face Weld Bead | <br>Face Weld Bead | <br>Face Weld Bead |
| Bead too small, with contour irregular.<br><br>Not enough weld metal in cross section.<br><br>Poor mechanical properties.<br><br>Undercut at toe lines of fillet. | Excessive bead width.<br><br>Overlapping without penetration at edges.<br><br>Fillet with unequal legs.<br><br>Wasted filler metal and productive time. | Excessive spatter and porosity.<br><br>Bead very irregular with poor penetration.<br><br>Weld metal not properly shielded.<br><br>Wasted electrode and productive time. |

# Examples of Good & Bad Welds
## – Flux Cored with External Shielding Gas

| GOOD<br>Proper Current<br>Voltage & Speed | BAD<br>Welding Current<br>Too Low<br>(High Voltage) | BAD<br>Welding Current<br>Too High<br>(Low Voltage) |
|---|---|---|
| <br>Cross-section Fillet | <br>Cross-section Fillet | <br>Cross-section Fillet |
| <br>Cross-section Weld Bead | <br>Cross-section Weld Bead | <br>Cross-section Weld Bead |
| <br>Face Weld Bead | <br>Face Weld Bead | <br>Face Weld Bead |
| A smooth, regular, well formed bead.<br><br>No undercutting, overlapping or pileup.<br><br>Uniform in cross section.<br><br>Excellent weld at minimal material and labor cost. | Excessive spatter and porosity.<br><br>Weld bead excessively wide and flat.<br><br>Undercutting along edges weakens joint.<br><br>Irregular bead contour. | Weld bead excessively convex and narrow.<br><br>Difficult slag removal.<br><br>Wasted filler metal and productive time. |

# Examples of Good & Bad Welds
## – Flux Cored with External Shielding Gas

| BAD<br>Welding Speed<br>Too Fast | BAD<br>Welding Speed<br>Too Slow | BAD<br>Insufficient<br>Shielding Gas Coverage |
|---|---|---|
| <br>Cross-section Fillet | <br>Cross-section Fillet | <br>Cross-section Fillet |
| <br>Cross-section Weld Bead | <br>Cross-section Weld Bead | <br>Cross-section Weld Bead |
| <br>Face Weld Bead | <br>Face Weld Bead | <br>Face Weld Bead |
| Bead too small, with contour irregular.<br><br>Not enough weld metal in cross section.<br><br>Poor mechanical properties.<br><br>Undercut at toe lines of fillet. | Excessive bead width.<br><br>Overlapping without penetration at edges.<br><br>Fillet with unequal legs.<br><br>Wasted filler metal and productive time. | Excessive spatter and porosity<br><br>Bead very irregular with poor penetration.<br><br>Weld metal not properly shielded.<br><br>Wasted electrode and productive time. |

# Examples of Good & Bad Welds
## – Gas Metal Arc Welding

| GOOD<br>Proper Current<br>Voltage & Speed | BAD<br>Welding Current<br>Too Low<br>(High Voltage) | BAD<br>Welding Current<br>Too High<br>(Low Voltage) |
|---|---|---|

Cross-section Fillet

Cross-section Fillet

Cross-section Fillet

Cross-section Weld Bead

Cross-section Weld Bead

Cross-section Weld Bead

Face Weld Bead

Face Weld Bead

Face Weld Bead

| | | |
|---|---|---|
| A smooth, regular, well formed bead.<br><br>No undercutting, overlapping or pileup.<br><br>Uniform in cross section.<br><br>Excellent weld at minimal material and labor cost. | Excessive piling up of weld metal.<br><br>Undercutting along edges weakens joint.<br><br>Irregular bead contour. | Weld bead excessively convex and wide.<br><br>Difficult removing silicon from face of weld.<br><br>Wasted filler metal and productive time.<br><br>Excessive spatter and porosity. |

# Examples of Good & Bad Welds
## – Gas Metal Arc Welding

| BAD<br>Welding Speed<br>Too Fast | BAD<br>Welding Speed<br>Too Slow | BAD<br>Insufficient<br>Shielding Gas Coverage |
|---|---|---|

Cross-section Fillet

Cross-section Fillet

Cross-section Fillet

Cross-section Weld Bead

Cross-section Weld Bead

Cross-section Weld Bead

Face Weld Bead

Face Weld Bead

Face Weld Bead

| | | |
|---|---|---|
| Bead too small, with contour irregular.<br><br>Not enough weld metal in cross section.<br><br>Poor mechanical properties.<br><br>Undercut at toe lines of fillet. | Excessive bead width.<br><br>Fillet with unequal legs.<br><br>Wasted filler metal and productive time. | Excessive spatter and porosity.<br><br>Weld bead very irregular with poor penetration.<br><br>Weld metal not properly shielded.<br><br>Wasted filler metal and time. |

# Examples of Good & Bad Welds
## – Metal Cored Welding

| GOOD<br>Proper Current<br>Voltage & Speed | BAD<br>Welding Current<br>Too Low<br>(High Voltage) | BAD<br>Welding Current<br>Too High<br>(Low Voltage) |
|---|---|---|

Cross-section Fillet

Cross-section Fillet

Cross-section Fillet

Cross-section Weld Bead

Cross-section Weld Bead

Cross-section Weld Bead

Face Weld Bead

Face Weld Bead

Face Weld Bead

A smooth, regular, well formed bead.

No undercutting, overlapping or pileup.

Uniform in cross section.

Excellent weld at minimal material and labor cost.

Excessive spatter and porosity.

Weld bead excessively wide and flat.

Undercutting along edges weakens joint.

Irregular bead contour.

Weld bead excessively convex and narrow.

Wasted filler metal and productive time.

# Examples of Good & Bad Welds
## – Metal Cored Welding

| **BAD**<br>Welding Speed<br>Too Fast | **BAD**<br>Welding Speed<br>Too Slow | **BAD**<br>Insufficient<br>Shielding Gas Coverage |
|---|---|---|
| <br>Cross-section Fillet | <br>Cross-section Fillet | <br>Cross-section Fillet |
| <br>Cross-section Weld Bead | <br>Cross-section Weld Bead | <br>Cross-section Weld Bead |
| <br>Face Weld Bead | <br>Face Weld Bead | <br>Face Weld Bead |
| Bead too small, with contour irregular.<br><br>Not enough weld metal in cross section.<br><br>Poor mechanical properties.<br><br>Undercut at toe lines of fillet. | Excessive bead width.<br><br>Overlapping without penetration at legs.<br><br>Fillet with unequal legs.<br><br>Wasted filler metal and productive time. | Excessive spatter and porosity.<br><br>Weld bead very irregular with poor penetration.<br><br>Weld metal not properly shielded.<br><br>Wasted filler metal and time. |

# Common Welding Problems: Causes and Cures

## porous welds

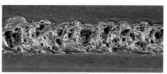

Why
1. Excessively long or short arc length.
2. Welding current too high.
3. Insufficient or damp shielding gas.
4. Too fast travel speed.
5. Base metal surface covered with oil, grease, moisture, rust, mill scale, etc.
6. Wet, unclean or damaged electrode.

What to do
1. Maintain proper arc length.
2. Use proper welding current.
3. Increase gas flow rate and check gas purity.
4. Reduce travel speed.
5. Properly clean base metal prior to welding.
6. Properly maintain and store electrode.

## cracked welds

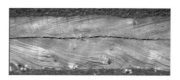

Why
1. Insufficient weld size.
2. Excessive joint restraint.
3. Poor joint design and/or preparation.
4. Filler metal does not match base metal.
5. Rapid cooling rate.
6. Base metal surface covered with oil, grease, moisture, rust, dirt or mill scale.

What to do
1. Adjust weld size to part thickness.
2. Reduce joint restraint through proper design.
3. Select the proper joint design
4. Use more ductile filler.
5. Reduce cooling rate through preheat.
6. Properly clean base metal prior to welding.

## undercutting

Why
1. Faulty electrode manipulation.
2. Welding current too high.
3. Too long an arc length.
4. Too fast travel speed.
5. Arc blow.

What to do
1. Pause at each side of the weld bead when using a weaving technique.
2. Use proper electrode angles.
3. Use proper welding current for electrode size and welding position.
4. Reduce arc length.
5. Reduce travel speed.
6. Reduce effects of arc blow

# Common Welding Problems: Causes and Cures

## distortion

Why
1. Improper tack welding and or faulty joint preparation.
2. Improper bead sequence.
3. Improper set-up and fixturing.
4. Excessive weld size.

What to do
1. Tack weld parts with allowance for distortion.
2. Use proper bead sequencing.
3. Tack or clamp parts securely.
4. Make welds to specified size.

## spatter

Why
1. Arc blow.
2. Welding current too high.
3. Too long an arc length.
4. Wet, unclean or damaged electrode.

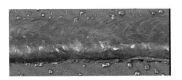

What to do
1. Attempt to reduce the effect of arc blow.
2. Reduce welding current.
3. Reduce arc length.
4. Properly maintain and store electrodes.

## lack of fusion

Why
1. Improper travel speed.
2. Welding current too low.
3. Faulty joint preparation.
4. Too large an electrode diameter.
5. Magnetic arc blow.
6. Wrong electrode angle.

What to do
1. Reduce travel speed.
2. Increase welding current.
3. Weld design should allow electrode accessibility to all surfaces within the joint.
4. Reduce electrode diameter.
5. Reduce effects of magnetic arc blow.
6. Use proper electrode angles.

# Common Welding Problems: Causes and Cures

## overlapping

Why
1. Too slow travel speed.
2. Incorrect electrode angle.
3. Too large an electrode.

What to do
1. Increase travel speed.
2. Use proper electrode angles.
3. Use a smaller electrode size.

---

## poor penetration

Why
1. Travel speed too fast.
2. Welding current too low.
3. Poor joint design and/or preparation.
4. Electrode diameter too large.
5. Wrong type of electrode.
6. Excessively long arc length.

What to do
1. Decrease travel speed.

2. Increase welding current.
3. Increase root opening or decrease rootface.
4. Use smaller electrode.
5. Use electrode w/deeper penetration characteristics.
6. Reduce arc length.

---

## inclusion

Why
1. Incomplete slag removal between passes.
2. Erratic travel speed.
3. Too wide a weaving motion.
4. Too large an electrode.
5. Letting slag run ahead of arc.
6. Tungsten spitting or sticking.

What to do
1. Completely remove slag between passes.

2. Use a uniform travel speed.
3. Reduce width of weaving technique.
4. Use a smaller electrode size for better access to joint.
5. Increase travel speed or change electrode angle or reduce arc length.
6. Properly prepare tungsten and use proper current.

# Check-Points for Quality Welding

The future of welding and the future of the welder's security rest upon quality welding. Public confidence in welding has been built up through the satisfactory service of millions and millions of welds. Public confidence can quickly be destroyed by a catastrophe that could be caused by a defective weld. Adherence to the following rules will insure quality welds and the future of the welding industry as well as your own job security.

1. Use only high quality welding machines, electrodes and welding accessories.

2. Know the base material that you are working on.

3. Select the proper welding process to give the highest quality welds on the base material to be used.

4. Select the proper welding procedure to meet the service requirement of the finished weldment.

5. Select the correct electrode for the job in question. See additional information concerning this elsewhere in this booklet.

6. When preheating is specified or required make sure that the temperature requirements are met. In any case do not weld on material below 32° F, without first preheating.

7. Clean the base metal of all slag, paint, grease, oil, moisture, and any other foreign materials.

8. Remove weld slag and thoroughly clean each bead prior to making the next bead or pass.

9. Do not weld over cracks or porous tack welds. Defective tack welds should be removed prior to welding.

10. Be particularly alert to obtain root fusion on the first pass of fillet and groove welds.

11. When root gaps of groove welds are excessive, build up one side of the joint prior to welding the pieces together.

12. When the root gap is excessive in fillet welding, be sure to increase the size of the fillet weld the amount of the root gap in order to maintain the strength requirement. In some cases it is an advantage to make a groove weld in order to avoid extremely large fillets.

13. Inspect work and immediately remove any defective weld and replace it.

14. Observe the size requirement for each weld and make sure that you meet or slightly exceed the specified size.

15. Make sure that the finished appearance of the weld is smooth and that overlaps and undercuts have been properly repaired. Remember that many people judge the strength of a weld merely by its external appearance.

# Troubleshooting Guide for Semiautomatic Wire Welding

| Desired Characteristic | | Arc Voltage | Welding Current | Travel Speed | Nozzle Angle | Tip-to-Work Distance | Wire Size | Gas Type |
|---|---|---|---|---|---|---|---|---|
| Deeper penetration | | | 1. Increase | | 3. Trailing Max. 25° | 2. Decrease | 5. Smaller[a] | 4. CO$_2$ |
| Shallower Penetration | | | 1. Decrease | | 3. Leading | 2. Increase | 5. Larger[a] | 4. Ar+CO$_2$[c] |
| Bead Height and Width | Larger Bead | | 1. Increase | 2. Decrease | | 3. Increase[a] | | |
| | Smaller Bead | | 1. Decrease | 2. Increase | | 3. Decrease[a] | | |
| | Higher, Narrower | 1. Increase | | | 2. Trailing | 3. Increase | | |
| | Flatter, Wider | 1. Decrease | | | 2. 90° or Leading | 3. Decrease | | |
| Faster Deposition Rate | | | 1. Increase | | | 2. Increase[a] | 3. Smaller[b] | |
| Slower Deposition Rate | | | 1. Decrease | | | 2. Decrease[a] | 3. Larger[b] | |

Key: 1. first choice, 2. second choice, 3. third choice, 4. fourth choice, and 5. fifth choice.

a) When these variables are changed, the wire feed speed must be adjusted so that the welding current remains constant. See deposition rate section of welding variables section.

b) See deposition rate section of welding variables section.

c) This change is especially helpful on materials 20 gauge and smaller thickness.

# Types of Joints

There are only 5 basic types of joints. They can, however, be used in combinations.

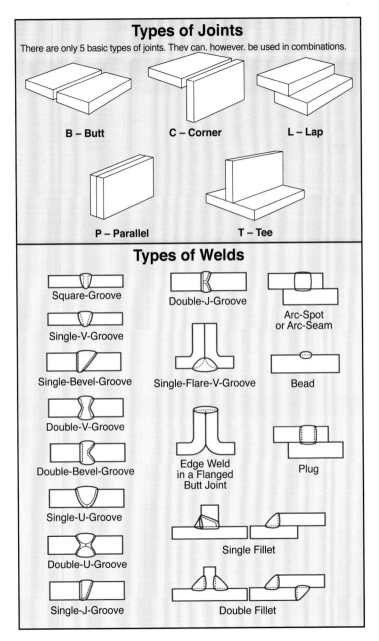

**B – Butt**

**C – Corner**

**L – Lap**

**P – Parallel**

**T – Tee**

# Types of Welds

Square-Groove

Single-V-Groove

Single-Bevel-Groove

Double-V-Groove

Double-Bevel-Groove

Single-U-Groove

Double-U-Groove

Single-J-Groove

Double-J-Groove

Single-Flare-V-Groove

Edge Weld
in a Flanged
Butt Joint

Arc-Spot
or Arc-Seam

Bead

Plug

Single Fillet

Double Fillet

33

# Weld Test Positions

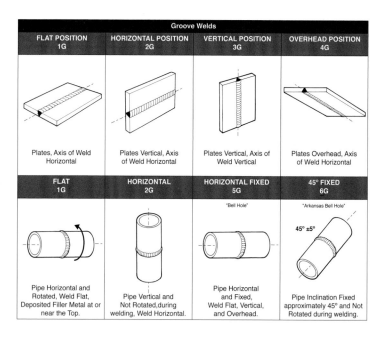

**Fillet Welds**

| FLAT POSITION 1F | HORIZONTAL POSITION 2F | VERTICAL POSITION 3F | OVERHEAD POSITION 4F |
|---|---|---|---|
| Axis of Weld Horizontal | Axis of Weld Horizontal | Axis of Weld Vertical | Axis of Weld Horizontal |

**Groove Welds**

| FLAT POSITION 1G | HORIZONTAL POSITION 2G | VERTICAL POSITION 3G | OVERHEAD POSITION 4G |
|---|---|---|---|
| Plates, Axis of Weld Horizontal | Plates Vertical, Axis of Weld Horizontal | Plates Vertical, Axis of Weld Vertical | Plates Overhead, Axis of Weld Horizontal |

| FLAT 1G | HORIZONTAL 2G | HORIZONTAL FIXED 5G | 45° FIXED 6G |
|---|---|---|---|
| | | "Bell Hole" | "Arkansas Bell Hole" |
| | | | 45° ±5° |
| Pipe Horizontal and Rotated, Weld Flat, Deposited Filler Metal at or near the Top. | Pipe Vertical and Not Rotated, during welding, Weld Horizontal. | Pipe Horizontal and Fixed, Weld Flat, Vertical, and Overhead. | Pipe Inclination Fixed approximately 45° and Not Rotated during welding. |

# Welding Codes & Qualification of Welders

Before a welder can begin work on any job covered by a welding code, qualification under the code that applies is required. Many different codes are in use and it is required that the specific code is referred to when taking qualification tests. In general the following type of work is covered by codes: pressure vessels and pressure piping, highway and railway bridges, public buildings, tanks and containers that will hold flammable or explosive materials, cross country pipelines, aircraft, ordinance material, ships and boats, and nuclear facilities. A qualified welding procedure is normally required.

Qualification is obtained differently under the various codes. Qualification under one code will not necessarily qualify a welder to weld under a different code. Qualification for an employer will not allow the welder to work for another employer (except in cases where welders are qualified by an association of employers). If the welder uses a different process or if the welding procedure is altered drastically, requalification is required. In most codes, if the welder is continually welding with the qualified procedure, welding requalification is not required, providing the work performed meets the quality requirement. An exception is the military aircraft code which requires periodical requalification.

Qualification tests may be given by responsible manufacturers or contractors. The welding procedure must be qualified before the welders can be qualified. To become qualified, the welder must make specified welds using the qualified welding procedure.

The welding procedures include information such as : process, base metal, thickness, electrode type position and joint design. In government specifications, a government inspector may witness the making of weld specimens. Specimens must be properly identified and prepared for testing.

The most common test is the guided bend test. In some cases radiographic (x-ray) examinations, fracture test or other tests are employed. Satisfactory completion of test specimens, providing they meet acceptability standards, will qualify the welder for specific types of welding. The welding allowed depends on the particular code. In general, the code indicates the range of thicknesses and the alloys which may be welded, and the positions which may be employed.

The qualification of welders is an extremely technical subject and cannot be adequately covered in this short publication. The actual code must be obtained and studied prior to taking the test.

The most widely used codes are: Structural Welding Code – AWS D1.1; Welding and Brazing Qualifications – Section IX of the ASME Boiler and Pressure Vessel Code; Standard for Welding Pipelines and Related Facilities – API 1104; American National Standard Code for Pressure Piping – ANSI B31.1; American Bureau of Shipping; Federal and Military Specifications. These codes can be obtained from the sponsoring association.

# Welding Symbols

AWS welding symbols are the shorthand of welding. They enable the engineer and draftsman to convey complete instructions-for-welding to the welder on blueprints and drawings.

Company-wide use of welding symbols will result in the following advantages:

**1.** Control of specific design instruction to the shop regarding weld sizes and plate edge preparation, eliminating the tendency for over-welding or under welding (resulting in either increased production costs or unsafe fabrication) because of lack of definite information.

**2.** Elimination of unnecessary details on drawings when such detail is for the sole purpose of indicating weld sizes and specifications. Welding notes will be minimized.

**3.** Establish a common understanding of design intent and requirements between engineering, shop, inspection, customer's representatives and code inspection authorities. The benefits of this advantage are readily apparent.

**4.** Standardization, not only within the company but industry-wise as well. AWS welding symbols are a national standard and are used worldwide.

The symbols shown on the following pages are from "Standard Symbols for Welding, Brazing, and Nondestructive Examination," A2.4, published by the American Welding Society.

# Location of Information on Welding Symbols

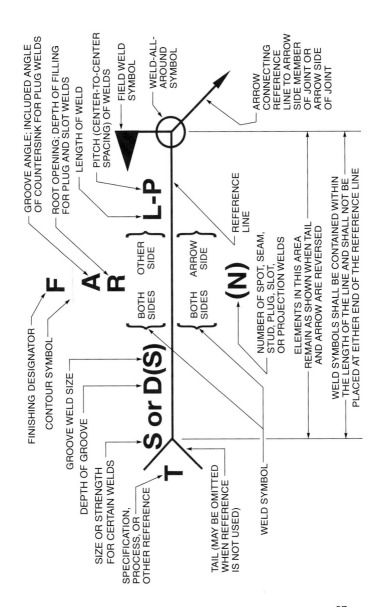

# Basic Welding Symbols and their Location Significance

| Type of Weld | | Arrow Side | Other Side | Both Sides | No Arrow Side or Other Side Significance |
|---|---|---|---|---|---|
| Fillet | | | | | not used |
| Plug or Slot | | | | not used | not used |
| Spot or Projection | | | | not used | |
| Stud | | | not used | not used | not used |
| Seam | | | | not used | |
| Back or Backing | | | | not used | not used |
| Surfacing | | | not used | not used | not used |
| Edge | | | | | not used |
| G R O O V E W E L D S | Square | | | | not used |
| | V | | | | not used |
| | Bevel | | | | not used |
| | U | | | | not used |
| | J | | | | not used |
| | Flare-V | | | | not used |
| | Flare Bevel | | | | not used |
| Scarf for Brazed Joint | | | | | not used |

# Typical Welding Symbols

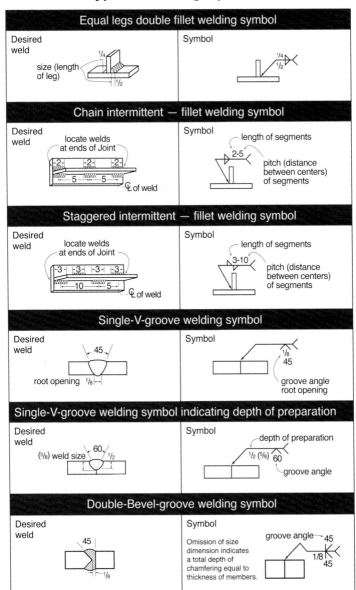

## Equal legs double fillet welding symbol

**Desired weld**

size (length of leg)

1/4

1/2

**Symbol**

1/4
1/2

## Chain intermittent — fillet welding symbol

**Desired weld**

locate welds at ends of Joint

-2- -2- -2-

5    5

℄ of weld

**Symbol**

length of segments

2-5

pitch (distance between centers) of segments

## Staggered intermittent — fillet welding symbol

**Desired weld**

locate welds at ends of Joint

-3- -3- -3- -3-

10    5

℄ of weld

**Symbol**

length of segments

3-10

pitch (distance between centers) of segments

## Single-V-groove welding symbol

**Desired weld**

45

root opening  1/8

**Symbol**

1/8
45

groove angle
root opening

## Single-V-groove welding symbol indicating depth of preparation

**Desired weld**

(5/8) weld size   60   1/2

**Symbol**

depth of preparation

1/2 (5/8)   60

groove angle

## Double-Bevel-groove welding symbol

**Desired weld**

45

1/8

**Symbol**

Omission of size dimension indicates a total depth of chamfering equal to thickness of members.

groove angle   45

1/8

45

# Typical Welding Symbols

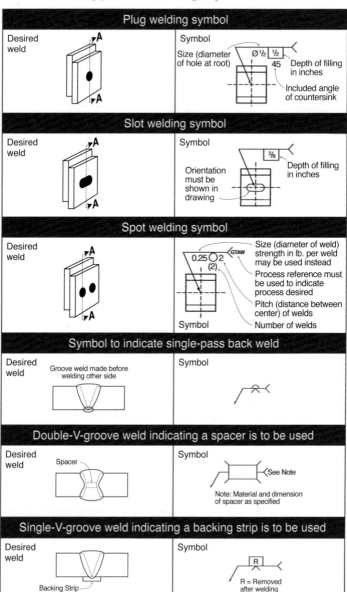

## Plug welding symbol

Desired weld

Symbol

Size (diameter of hole at root)

Ø½  ½

45

Depth of filling in inches

Included angle of countersink

## Slot welding symbol

Desired weld

Symbol

Orientation must be shown in drawing

⅜

Depth of filling in inches

## Spot welding symbol

Desired weld

0.25 ○ 2
(2)

GTAW

Size (diameter of weld) strength in lb. per weld may be used instead

Process reference must be used to indicate process desired

Pitch (distance between center) of welds

Number of welds

Symbol

## Symbol to indicate single-pass back weld

Desired weld

Groove weld made before welding other side

Symbol

## Double-V-groove weld indicating a spacer is to be used

Desired weld

Spacer

Symbol

See Note

Note: Material and dimension of spacer as specified

## Single-V-groove weld indicating a backing strip is to be used

Desired weld

Backing Strip

Symbol

R

R = Removed after welding

# Typical Welding Symbols

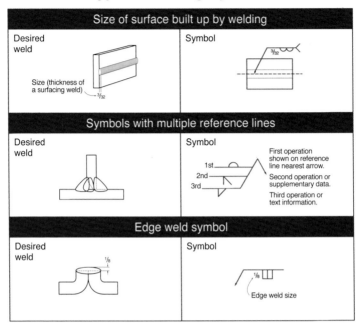

## Size of surface built up by welding

**Desired weld**

Size (thickness of a surfacing weld) — 3/32

**Symbol**

3/32

## Symbols with multiple reference lines

**Desired weld**

**Symbol**

1st
2nd
3rd

First operation shown on reference line nearest arrow.

Second operation or supplementary data.

Third operation or text information.

## Edge weld symbol

**Desired weld**

1/8

**Symbol**

1/8

Edge weld size

# Supplementary Welding Symbols

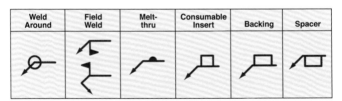

| Weld Around | Field Weld | Melt-thru | Consumable Insert | Backing | Spacer |
|---|---|---|---|---|---|

| Contour | | |
|---|---|---|
| Flush or Flat | Convex | Concave |

# General Welding Safety

Essentially, welding is not a hazardous occupation if proper precautionary measures are always observed. This requires continuous awareness of possibilities of danger and habitual safety precaution by the welders. They have an obligation to learn safe practices, to obey safety rules and regulations, and to work in a safe manner. It is the responsibility of supervisors to enforce safety rules and regulations set forth in ANSI Z49.1 available from http://www.aws.org.

The Occupational Safety and Health Administration (OSHA) requires that employers must have a comprehensive hazard communication program to inform employees about hazardous substances that might be used in the workplace. The purpose of the Safety Data Sheets (SDS) is to explain the hazards involved in handling/using products such as welding consumables and the precautionary measures which must be put in place for safe welding.

| For Goggles or Helmet | | Shade No. |
|---|---|---|
| Operation | | |
| Soldering | | 2 |
| Torch Brazing | | 3 or 4 |
| Oxygen Cutting | Up to 1 inch | 3 or 4 |
| | 1-6 inches | 4 or 5 |
| | 6 inches and over | 5 or 6 |
| Gas Welding | Up to 1 inch | 4 or 5 |
| | 1-6 inches | 5 or 6 |
| | 6 inches and over | 6 or 8 |
| Nonferrous Metal Welding | Gas Metal Arc Welding (GMAW, TIG) | |
| | Gas Metal Arc Welding (GMAW, MIG) 1/16", 3/32", 1/8" and 5/32" electrodes | 11 |
| | Plasma Arc Welding (PAW) | |
| Ferrous Metal Welding | Gas Metal Arc Welding (GMAW, TIG) | |
| | Gas Metal Arc Welding (GMAW, MIG) 1/16", 3/32", 1/8" and 5/32" electrodes | 11 |
| | Plasma Arc Welding (PAW) | |
| Shielded Metal Arc Welding (SMAW, Stick) | 1/16", 3/32", 1/8" and 5/32" electrodes | 10 |
| | 1/16", 7/32" and 1/4" electrodes | 12 |
| | 5/16" and 3/8" electrodes | 14 |

## Safety Precautions for Arc Welding

1. Make sure your arc welding equipment is installed properly and grounded and is in good working condition.
2. Always wear protective clothing suitable for the welding to be done.
3. Always wear proper eye protection when welding, cutting, or grinding. Do not look at the arc without proper eye protection.
4. Avoid breathing the air in the fume plume directly above the arc.
5. Keep your work area clean and free of hazards. Make sure that no flammable, volatile, or explosive materials are in or near the work area.

6. Handle all compressed gas cylinders with extreme care. Keep caps on when not in use.

7. Make sure that compressed gas cylinders are secured to the wall or other structural supports.

8. When compressed gas cylinders are empty, close the valve and mark the cylinder "empty".

9. Do not weld in a confined space without taking special precautions.

10. Do not weld on containers that have held combustibles without taking special precautions.

11. Do not weld on sealed containers or compartments without providing vents and taking special precautions.

12. Use mechanical exhaust at the point of welding when welding lead, cadmium, chromium, manganese, brass, bronze, zinc, or galvanized steel, and when welding in a confined space.

13. When it is necessary to weld in a damp or wet area, wear rubber boots and stand on a dry, insulated platform.

14. Do not use cables with frayed, cracked or bare spots in the insulation.

15. When the electrode holder is not in use, hang it on brackets provided. Never let it touch a compressed gas cylinder.

16. Dispose of electrode stubs in proper containers since stubs on the floor are a safety hazard.

17. Shield others from the light rays produced by your welding arc.

18. Do not weld near degreasing operations.

19. When working above ground, make sure that scaffold, ladder or work surface is solid and properly secured.

20. When welding in high places, use a safety belt or lifeline.

**Safety Precautions for Oxyacetylene Welding and Cutting**

1. Make sure that all gas apparatus shows UL or FM approval, is installed properly, and is in good working condition. Make sure that all connections are tight before lighting the torch. Do not use a flame to inspect for tight joints. Use soap solution to detect leaks.

2. Always wear protective clothing suitable for welding or flame cutting.

3. Keep work area clean and free from hazardous materials. When flame cutting, sparks can travel 30 to 40 feet (10 to 15 m). Do not allow flame cut sparks to hit hoses, regulators, or cylinders.

4. Handle all compressed gas cylinders with extreme care. Keep cylinder caps on when not in use.

5. Make sure that all compressed gas cylinders are secured to the wall or to other structural supports. Keep acetylene cylinders in the vertical position.

6. Store compressed gas cylinders in a safe place with good ventilation. Acetylene cylinders and oxygen cylinders should be kept apart.

7. When compressed gas cylinders or fuel gas cylinders are empty, close the valve and mark the cylinder "empty".

8. Use oxygen and acetylene or other fuel gases with the appropriate torches and only for the purpose intended.

9. Avoid breathing the air in the fume plume directly above the flame.

10. Never use acetylene at a pressure in excess of 15 psi (103.4 K Pa). Higher pressure can cause an explosion.

11. Never use oil, grease, or any material on any apparatus or threaded fittings in the oxyacetylene or oxyfuel system. Oil and grease in contact with oxygen may cause spontaneous combustion..

12. Do not weld or flame cut in a confined space without taking special precautions.

13. When assembling apparatus, crack gas cylinder valve before attaching regulators (cracking means opening the valve on the cylinder slightly, then closing.) This blows out any accumulated foreign material. Make sure that all threaded fittings are clean and tight.

14. Always use this correct sequence and technique for lighting a torch:

   (a) Open acetylene cylinder valve.

   (b) Open acetylene torch valve 1/4 turn.

   (c) Screw in acetylene regulator, adjusting valve handle to working pressure.

   (d) Turn off acetylene torch valve (you will have purged the acetylene line).

   (e) Slowly open oxygen cylinder valve all the way.

   (f) Open oxygen torch valve 1/4 turn.

   (g) Screw in oxygen regulator screw to working pressure.

   (h) Turn off oxygen torch valve (you will have purged the oxygen line).

(i) Open acetylene torch valve 1/4 turn and light with lighter (use friction-type lighter or special provided lighting device only).

(j) Open oxygen torch valve 1/4 turn.

(k) Adjust to neutral flame.

15. Always use this correct sequence and technique of shutting off a torch:

   (a) Close acetylene torch valve first. Then close oxygen torch valve.

   (b) Close cylinder valves -- the acetylene valve first, then the oxygen valve.

   (c) Open torch acetylene and oxygen valves (to release pressure in the regulator and hose).

   (d) Back off regulator adjusting valve handle until no spring tension is felt.

   (e) Close torch valves.

16. Use mechanical exhaust when welding or cutting lead, cadmium, chromium, manganese, brass, bronze, zinc, or galvanized steel.

17. If you must weld or flame cut with combustible or volatile materials present, take extra precautions, make out hot work permit, and provide for a lookout, etc.

18. Do not weld or flame cut on containers that have held combustibles without taking special precautions.

19. Do not weld or flame cut into sealed container or compartment without providing vents and taking special precautions.

20. Do not weld or cut in a confined space without taking special precautions.

There must be continual vigilance over safety conditions and safety hazards. Safety meetings should be held regularly. The safety rules should be reissued annually and they must be completely understood and enforced. Safety rules and precautions should be posted in the welding shop.

# Welding Metals

Almost every metal known can be welded by one process or another. The arc welding processes used primarily for steels include Shielded Metal Arc Welding (SMAW), Gas Metal Arc Welding (GMAW) and Flux Cored Arc Welding (FCAW). Welding electrodes should be selected based on the composition of the steel to be welded. Steels are manufactured and specified in many different ways. In general, steels are classified according to the carbon content, that is, low carbon, medium carbon or high carbon steels. In addition they are also classified according to the type of alloy employed, such as chrome moly, nickel, manganese, etc. Steels are also sold under many trade names and specifications. The following is a brief listing of some of the specifications in use.

**ASTM** — The American Society for Testing and Materials sponsors specifications covering many different types of steels. Their specifications may be prefixed by their acronym of ASTM.

**API** —The American Petroleum Institute specifies steels usually employed in pipe.

**ASME** — The American Society of Mechanical Engineers specifies steels but in general utilize the same numbers as the ASTM specifications.

**Military and Federal Specification** — The Government specifications are usually indicated by the letters MIL or QQ.

**SAE and AISI** — The Society of Automotive Engineers and the American Iron and Steel Institute have a very complete listing of steels using code numbers that indicate the steel composition. Stainless steels are covered by the AISI numbers.

# Steel Available for Welding

Steel warehouses located in most larger cities carry stocks of the popular sizes and shapes of mild steel. Large requirements can be obtained direct from steel mills. The following is a listing of the various shapes, sizes and types usually available.

## Shapes — (Composition usually to ASTM Specs)
American Standard Beams — 6" to 24" – Specified: Depth by wt. per foot
Wide Flange Shapes 6" to 36" — Specified: Depth by wt. per foot
American Standard Channels — 3" to 18" – Specified: Depth by wt. per foot
Angles (equal and unequal legs) — 1 x 1 to 8 x 8 leg by leg by thickness
Structural Tees — These are split beams or wide flange shapes.
Misc. Light and Junior Sections — Lighter and thinner than above.
Misc. Sections such as Zee's, pilings, rails, etc.

## Bars — (Composition usually to AISI or SAE Specs)
Flats thickness — 1/4" to 4" by width 3/8" to 8"
Square — 1/4" sq.: to 2 3/4" sq. — Special 1/2" sq. to 6" square.
Rounds — 3/16" dia. to 2 7/8" dia. — Special 3/8" dia. to 9 1/2" dia.
Half Rounds — 1/2" to 3" (across diameter)
Hexagons — 1/2" to 1 3/8" (across flats)

## Tubular — (Composition usually to ASTM or API Specs)
Pipe — Specified by nominal pipe diameter in inches.
 Wall thickness specified by Schedule Number or by Standard,
 Extra Strong or Double Extra Strong
Round Tubing — Seamless Mechanical
 3/16" dia. O.D. wall thickness 24 gage to 16 gage to 10" dia. O.D. wall thickness 1/4" to 1 1/8".
Round Tubing — Welded Mechanical
 3/8" dia. O.D. wall thickness 22 gage to 16 gage, to 6" dia.
 O.D. wall thickness 11 gage to 1/4"
Square Tubing — Mechanical and Structural — Welded or Seamless
 1/2" to 1/2" wall thickness 20 gage to 16 gage, to 4" x 4" wall thickness 11 gage to 3/16".
Rectangular Tubing — Welded Mechanical
 1 1/2" x 1" wall thickness 14 gage, to 4" x 2" wall thickness 3/16".

## Sheet and Plates — (Composition usually to ASTM or chemistry for end use)
Widths beyond 8 inches are considered sheet or plate — thickness above 3/16" considered plates. Sheets specified by gage thickness. Plates specified by thickness in inches or weight per square foot.

## Misc.
Warehouses offer many other forms of steel such as dished heads for tanks, reinforcing rods, etc. and flame cutting service.
Note — Trade names are often used to identify steel compositions.

# Identification of Metals

| Test / Metal | Low carbon mild steel | Medium carbon steel | High carbon armor steel | Chrome molybdenum steel |
|---|---|---|---|---|
| Appearance | Dark grey | Dark grey | Dark grey | Dark grey |
| Magnetic | Strongly magnetic | Strongly magnetic | Strongly magnetic | Strongly magnetic |
| Chisel | Continuous chip, smooth edges, chips easily | Continuous chip, smooth edges, chips easily | Hard to chip, can be continuous | Continuous chip, smooth edges, chips easily |
| Fracture | Bright grey | Very light grey | Very light grey | Bright grey, fine grain |
| Flame | Melts fast, becomes bright red before melting | Melts fast, becomes bright red before melting | Melts fast, becomes bright red before melting | Melts fast, becomes bright red before melting |
| Spark | Long yellow spark stream (Approx. 20% carbon or below) | Yellow lines, sprigs (Approx. .20% to .45% carbon) | Yellow lines, bright burst very clear (approx. .45% carbon and above) | Smaller spark stream, minor branching |

# Identification of Metals

| Test \ Metal | High manganese steel | Stainless steel | Cast iron | Titanium |
|---|---|---|---|---|
| Appearance | Dark cast surface | Bright, silvery, smooth | Dull grey, evidence of sand mold | Bright, silvery |
| Magnetic | Non-magnetic | Depends on exact analysis | Strongly magnetic | Non-magnetic |
| Chisel | Extremely hard to chisel | Continuous chip, smooth, bright color | Small chips about 1/8", not easy to chip, brittle | Hard to chisel |
| Fracture | Course grained | Depends on type, bright | Brittle | Bright silver |
| Flame | Melts fast, becomes bright red before melting | Melts fast, becomes bright red before melting | Melts fast, becomes bright red before melting | Shavings may burn |
| Spark | Bright yellow/white spark stream, minor branching | Very small spark stream, not bright | Curved yellow spark lines, yellow, not bright | Very bright white spark stream with white star bursts |

49

# Typical Preheat for Various Metals

| Base Metals Welded | Preheat |
|---|---|
| Low Carbon and Mild Steel | 70-100°F (21-38°C) |
| Medium Carbon Steel | 250-500°F (120-260°C) |
| High Carbon Steel | 500-600°F (260-315°C) |
| Low Alloy Nickel Steel<br>    Less than 1/4 in. (6.4mm) thick<br>    Over 1/4 in (6.4mm) thick | <br>70-100°F (21-30°C)<br>500°F (260°C) |
| Carbon content below .20% | 200-300°F (92-150°C) |
| Carbon Content .20% to .35% | 600-800°F (315-425°C) |
| Carbon Content over .35% | 900-1100°F (480-595°C) |
| Low Alloy Manganese Steel | 400-600°F (205-315°C) |
| Low Alloy Chromium Steel | 70-100°F (21-38°C) |
| Low Alloy Molybdenum Steel<br>    Carbon Content below .15%<br>    Carbon Content above /15% | <br>70-100°F (21-38°C)<br>400-600°F (205-315°C) |
| High Strength Low Alloy Steel | 150-300°F 66-150°C) |
| Austenitic Stainless Steel | 70-100°F (21-30°C) |
| Ferritic Stainless Steel | 150-500°FG (66-260°C) |
| Martensitic Stainless Steel | 150-600°F (66-315°C) |
| Cast Irons | 500-1100°F (260-595°C) |
| Copper and Copper Alloys | 500-800°F (260-425°C) |
| Nickel and Nickel Alloys | 70-100°F (21-38°C) |
| Aluminum and Aluminum Alloys | 70-100°F (21-38°C) |
| Magnesium Alloys | 70-100°F (21-38°C) |

Notes:

1. A preheat of up to 225°F (107°C) may be used for very thick sections, high joint restraint, and for removal of water condensation.

2. A preheat of up to 300°F (150°C) may be used for welding on thick sections to compensate for the high thermal conductivity of aluminum.

3. A preheat of 500-750°F (260-400°C) may be used for thin and highly restrained joints.

# AISI-SAE Designation System for Carbon and Alloy Steels

| Digits | Type of Steel | Nominal % of Alloy Content |
|--------|---------------|----------------------------|
| 10XX | Plain carbon | 1.00% Mn, max. |
| 11XX | Resulfurized | .08-.13 C & .50-.80 Mn |
| 12XX | Resulfurized and rephosphorized | 1.3 C & .60-.90 Mn |
| 13XX | Manganese | 1.75 Mn |
| 15XX | Plain carbon steel | 1.00-1.65 Mn |
| 23XX | Nickel steel | 3.50 Ni |
| 25XX | Nickel steel | 5.00 Ni |
| 31XX | Nickel-chromium steel | 1.25 Ni, .65 & .80Cr |
| 32XX | Nickel-chromium steel | 1.75 Ni, 1.07 Cr |
| 33XX | Nickel-chromium steel | 3.50 Ni, 1.50 & 1.57 Cr |
| 34XX | Nickel-chromium steel | 3.00 Ni, .77 Cr |
| 40XX | Molybdenum steel | .20 & .25 Mo |
| 41XX | Chromium-molybdenum steel | .50, .80 & .90 Cr, .12,.20, .25 & .30 Mo |
| 43XX | Nickel-chromium-molybdenum steel | 1.82 Ni, .50 & .80Cr, .25 Mo |
| 43BVXX | Nickel-chromium-molybdenum steel | 1.82 Ni, .50 & .80 Cr, .12 & .25 Mo, .03 V |
| 44XX | Molybdenum steel | .40& .52 Mo |
| 46XX | Nickel-molybdenum steel | 1.05 Ni, .45 Cr, .20 & .35 Mo |
| 47XX | Nickel-chromium-molybdenum steel | 1.05 Ni, .45 Cr, .20 & .35 Mo |
| 50XX | Chromium steel | .27, .40, .50 &.65 Cr |
| 51XX | Chromium steel | .80, .87, .92, 1.00 & 1.05 Cr |
| 50XXX | Chromium steel | .50 Cr, 1.00 C min |
| 51XXX | Chromium steel | 1.02 Cr, 1.00 C min |
| 52XXX | Chromium steel | 1.45 Cr, 1.00 C min |
| 61XX | Chromium-vanadium steel | .60, .80 & .95 Cr; .10 & .15 V min |
| 72XX | Tungsten-chromium steel | 1.75 W, .75 Cr |
| 81XX | Nickel-chromium-molybdenum steel | .30 Ni, .40 Cr, .12 Mo |
| 86XX | Nickel-chromium-molybdenum steel | .55 Ni, .50 Cr, .20 Mo |
| 87XX | Nickel-chromium-molybdenum steel | .55, .50 Cr, .25 Mo |
| 88XX | Nickel-chromium-molybdenum steel | .55 Ni, .50 Cr, .35 Mo |
| 92XX | Silicon-manganese steel | 1.40 & 2.00 Si; .65, .82 & .85 Mn; .00 & .65 Cr |
| 93XX | Nickel-chromium-molybdenum steel | 3.25 Ni, 1.20 Cr, .12 Mo |
| 94XX | Nickel-chromium-molybdenum steel | .45 Ni, .40 Xe, .12 Mo |
| 97XX | Nickel-chromium-molybdenum steel | .55 Ni, .20 Cr, .20 Mo |
| 98XX | Nickel-chromium-molybdenum steel | 1.00 Ni, .80 Cr, .25 Mo |

*Extracted from "Weldability of Steels" by R.D. Stout, 1987. Welding Research Council, New York, NY.*

# Cost Saving Tips

Welding is the most economical method of joining metals. However, we should all be on the lookout for ways to save time and materials to make welding the most advantageous. The following hints will help to lower arc welding costs.

**Material** — Select an easily weldable material that will not require expensive electrodes or complicated welding procedures.

**Joint Design** — On heavier material, double bevel and V joints save considerable weld material. Of course, it is necessary to be able to weld both sides.

**Rolled Sections and Forming** — Use bends and rolled angle channels, etc., to reduce the number of weld joints required.

**Distortion Control** — Use wandering or back step sequence to reduce warpage and keep material in line to reduce the machining necessary.

**Proper Fit-up** — Wide gaps between pieces to be welded waste weld metal. Fillets must be increased by the amount of gap to maintain strength.

**Fillet Weld Size** — Fillet weld size must be closely controlled. Doubling the size of a fillet requires four times as much weld metal.

**Convexity**    **Reinforcement**

**Convexity and Reinforcement** — Extra reinforcement and unequal legged fillets waste weld metal. The crown or reinforcement adds little to the strength of the weld.

**Positioning** — Position the job for flat welding if at all possible. This is the most efficient position. It allows use of larger electrodes. It is easier and more comfortable for the welder.

**Arc Length** — Keep a short arc or low voltage. This will concentrate all of the welding current in the joint and will minimize spatter.

**Electrode Type** — Select the higher production type electrode for cost savings. See description in electrode section of booklet.

# Use Largest Size Electrode Possible

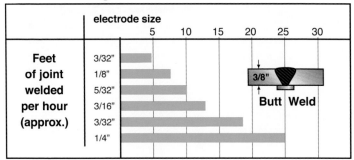

**Electrode Size** — Use the largest size electrode possible. Large size stick electrodes cost less and increase the welding speed. This is generally true in wire electrodes.

**Stub Ends** — Burn electrodes to a 2 inch length or use the continuous wire electrodes.

**Machine Efficiency** — Match the welding machine to the job. Too small a machine is inefficient since it may be operated beyond its capacity. Machines should be checked periodically for loose connections, wire, etc.

**Loose Connections** — Check cables, connectors, electrode holders for hot spots. Loose connections or broken wire will show up as hot spots which waste power. Correct them when found.

**Cable Size and Length** — Too small welding cable will heat up. Heat produced in the cable is wasteful. It is not doing useful work. Cables that are too long waste power, and causes a voltage drop at the holder. Excessive cable wrapped in coils is also very wasteful. Use the proper size cable and keep cable to reasonable lengths for efficiency.

## Suggested power cable size guide

| Input Ampere Rating of Welder | | | Power Cable Wire Size A.W.G. |
|---|---|---|---|
| Motor Driven Three Phase | Rectifier or Transform Single Phase | Rectifier or Transform Three Phase | |
| Up to 24A | Up to 30A | Up to 24A | 10 |
| 24 to 32A | 30 to 40A | 24 to 32A | 8 |
| 32 to 44A | 40 to 55A | 32 to 44A | 6 |
| 44 to 64A | 55 to 70A | 44 to 64A | 4 |
| 64 to 76A | 70 to 95A | 64 to 76A | 2 |
| 76 to 88A | 95 to 110A | 76 yo 88A | 1 |
| 88 to 100A | 110 to 125A | 88 to 100A | 1/0 |
| 100 to 130A | 125 to 165A | 100 to 130A | 2/0 |
| 130 to 155A | 185 to 195A | 130 to 155A | 4/0 |

AWG = AmericanWire Gauge.
*Source: NFPA 70: National Electrical Code. National Fire Protection Association. Quincy, MA.*

## Suggested copper welding cable size guide

| Weld Type | Weld Current | \multicolumn{6}{c}{Length of Cable in Feet – Cable Size A.W.G.} |
|---|---|---|---|---|---|---|---|

| Weld Type | Weld Current | 60' | 100' | 150' | 200' | 300' | 400' |
|---|---|---|---|---|---|---|---|
| Manual (Low Duty Cycle) | 100 | 4 | 4 | 4 | 2 | 1 | 1/0 |
| | 150 | 2 | 2 | 2 | 1 | 2/0 | 3/0 |
| | 200 | 2 | 2 | 1 | 1/0 | 3/0 | 4/0 |
| | 250 | 2 | 2 | 1/0 | 2/0 | | |
| | 300 | 1 | 1 | 2/0 | 3/0 | | |
| | 350 | 1/0 | 1/0 | 3/0 | 4/0 | | |
| | 400 | 1/0 | 1/0 | 3/0 | | | |
| | 450 | 2/0 | 2/0 | 4/0 | | | |
| | 500 | 2/0 | 2/0 | 4/0 | | | |
| Automatic (High Duty Cycle) | 400 | 4/0 | 4/0 | | | | |
| | 800 | 4/0 (2) | 4/0 (2) | | | | |
| | 1200 | 4/0 (3) | 4/0 (3) | | | | |
| | 1600 | 4/0 (4) | 4/0 (4) | | | | |

Note: Length of cable circuit equals total electrode and work cable.

*Source: NFPA 70: National Electrical Code. National Fire Protection Association. Quincy, MA.*

## Voltage drop per 100 feet of lead

| Welding Current Amperes | \multicolumn{6}{c}{Cable Size (A.W.G.) and Voltage Drop} |
|---|---|---|---|---|---|---|

| Welding Current Amperes | 2 | 1 | 1/0 | 2/0 | 3/0 | 4/0 |
|---|---|---|---|---|---|---|
| 50 | 1.0 | 0.7 | 0.5 | 0.4 | 0.3 | .03 |
| 75 | 1.3 | 1.0 | 0.8 | 0.7 | 0.5 | .04 |
| 100 | 1.8 | 1.4 | 1.2 | 0.9 | 0.7 | .06 |
| 125 | 2.3 | 1.7 | 1.4 | 1.1 | 1.0 | .07 |
| 150 | 2.8 | 2.1 | 1.7 | 1.4 | 1.1 | .09 |
| 175 | 3.3 | 2.8 | 2.0 | 1.7 | 1.3 | 1.0 |
| 200 | 3.7 | 3.0 | 2.4 | 2.0 | 1.5 | 1.2 |
| 250 | 4.7 | 3.6 | 3.0 | 2.4 | 1.8 | 1.5 |
| 300 | | 4.4 | 3.4 | 2.8 | 2.2 | 1.7 |
| 350 | | | 4.0 | 3.2 | 2.5 | 2.0 |
| 400 | | | 4.6 | 3.7 | 2.9 | 2.3 |
| 450 | | | | 4.2 | 3.2 | 2.6 |
| 500 | | | | 4.7 | 3.6 | 2.8 |
| 550 | | | | | 3.9 | 3.1 |
| 600 | | | | | 4.3 | 3.4 |
| 650 | | | | | | 3.7 |
| 700 | | | | | | 4.0 |

*Source: NFPA 70: National Electrical Code. National Fire Protection Association. Quincy, MA.*

# 8 Factors to Consider When Selecting Electrodes

1. Base Metal Strength Properties
2. Base Metal Composition
3. Welding Position
4. Welding Current
5. Joint Design and Fit-up
6. Thickness and Shape of Base Metal
7. Service Condition and/or Specifications
8. Production Efficiency and Job Conditions

### 1. Base Metal Strength Properties
Know and match mechanical properties. Mild steel — generally E-60XX or E-70XX electrodes match base metal. Low alloy steel — select electrodes that match base metal properties.

### 2. Base Metal Composition
Know and match composition. Mild steel — any E-60XX or E-70XX electrode is satisfactory. Low alloy steel — select electrode that most closely matches base metal composition.

### 3. Welding Position
Match electrode to welding position encountered.

### 4. Welding Current
Match power supply available. Some electrodes are designed for direct current (DC); others, alternating current (AC); some, either. Observe correct polarity.

### 5. Joint Design and Fit-up
Select for penetration characteristic — digging, medium, or light. No beveling or tight fit-up — use digging. Thin material or wide root opening — light, soft arc.

### 6. Thickness And Shape of Base Metal
To avoid weld cracking on thick and heavy material of complicated design, select electrode with maximum ductility. Low hydrogen processes or electrodes are recommended.

### 7. Service Condition and/or Specifications
Determine service conditions — low temperature, high temperature, shock loading — match base metal composition, ductility and impact resistance. Use low hydrogen process. Also, check welding procedure or specification for electrode type.

### 8. Production Efficiency and Job Conditions
For high deposition and most efficient production under flat position requirements, select high iron powder types or large diameter wires: For other conditions, you may need to experiment with various electrodes and sizes.

# Metal Cored Wire

Edited from an article by Steve Barhorst and
used with permission from Hobart Brothers Company.

Metal cored wire is a tubular electrode that consists of a metal sheath and a core of various powdered materials, primarily iron. The core contributes almost entirely to the deposited weld metal.

### What applications benefit from metal cored wire?

- Solid wire in the flat and horizontal positions where spray transfer is being used.

- Many gas shielded, flux cored, and some submerged arc applications.

- Multiple-pass robotic and automatic welding

- Other applications determined by weld cost calculations or quality issues (compensating for poor fit-up, bead appearance, burn-through).

### Why use metal cored wire?

- Can save $100 to $200 for every 100 pounds of weld metal deposited.

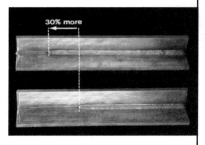

- High deposition rates and travel speeds.

- No slag; almost no spatter.

- Little or no post-weld cleanup or cleaning between passes.

- Excellent side-wall fusion and root penetration.

- Ability to bridge part gaps without burn-through.

- Ability to weld thin materials at high amperages without burn-through.

- Capability to weld out-of-position with pulsed spray or short-circuit transfer.

- Compliance with ABS, DNV, API, LRS, ANSI, and AWS standards.

**Solid Wire**

**Metal Cored Wire**

## Oven storage and reconditioning of stick electrodes

| Item Designation | Storage of Contents of Open Cartons* | Reconditioning* |
|---|---|---|
| Mild Steel – 6010, 6011 | Dry at room temperature | Not recommended |
| Mild Steel – 6013, 6022, 7014, 7024 | 100°F – 130°F | 250°F – 300°F, 1 hr. |
| Mild Steel Low Alloy – 7010, 8010, 9010 | Dry at room temperature | Not recommended |
| Mild Steel, Low Alloy, Low Hydrogen – 7018, 8018, 9015, 9018, 10018, 9010, 7018, 8018, 9015, 9018, 10018, 9010, 11018, 12018 | 250°F – 300°F | 500°F – 800°F, 1-2 hrs. |
| Stainless Steel Stick Electrodes DC Lime (AWS-15) Sterling AP & AC/DC (AWS-16) Smootharc Plus (AWS-16) Sterling (AWS-17) | 225°F – 260°F | 500°F – 600°F, 1 hr. |
| Hardalloy® Surfacing | 225°F – 260°F | 450°F – 600°F, 1 hr. |
| Special Maintenance GP | 225°F – 260°F | 500°F, 1 hr. |
| Cast Iron Electrodes | 215°F – 230°F | 250°F – 300°F, 1 hr. |

\* Remove any packaging that may be damaged from oven storage or reconditioning.

Welding electrodes may be damaged by atmospheric moisture. The following table recommends proper storage conditions, and time and temperature for reconditioning electrodes that have absorbed excess moisture.

**Notes for table:** Pallets and unopened cartons of electrodes should be stored away from exposure to water in the form of rain, snow, spray, or humidity. Only hermetically sealed cans are safe against these conditions. Damaged cartons permit entry of damp air which may be picked up by the product and lower its quality. Humidity below 50% should be avoided for 6010, 6011, 6012 and 6013 electrodes. At no time should these classes of electrodes be stored in an oven above 130°F.

The instruction, "Dry at Room Temperature" in the table signifies that the humidity should be below 70% and the temperature should be within the limits 40°F to 120°F.

# Shielding Gases and Their Uses

| Shielding Gas | Gas Composition | Gas Reaction | Application | Remarks |
|---|---|---|---|---|
| Argon | Air | Inert | Nonferrous metals | Least expensive inert gas, provides spray transfer |
| Argon + Helium | 50% Ar 50% He | Inert | Al, Mg, Copper & their alloys | Higher heat in arc use on heavier thickness – less porosity, provides spray transfer |
| Argon + Oxygen | Argon + 1-2% O | Oxidizing* | Stainless steel | Oxygen provides arc stability |
| Argon + Oxygen | Argon + 3.5% ) | Oxidizing | Mild & Low Alloy | Provides spray transfer |
| Argon + Carbon Dioxide | 75% Ar 25% $CO_2$ | Slightly oxidizing | Mild & Low Alloy Steels (also some stainless with GMAW) | Smooth weld surface, reduces penetration, short circuiting |
| Helium + Argon + Carbon Dioxide | 90% He + 7.5% Ar + 2.5% $CO_2$ | Essentially Inert | Stainless Steel and some Alloys | Provides arc stability, helpful in out of position welding, short circuiting |
| Helium + Argon | 75% He 25% Ar | Inert | Al, Mg, Copper & their Alloys | Higher heat input than Ar, minimum porosity |
| Carbon Dioxide | $CO_2$ | Oxidizing | Mild & Low Alloy steels (also some stainless steels) | Least expensive gas, deep penetration, short circuiting or globular |
| Nitrogen | $N_2$ | Essentially Inert | Copper & Copper Alloys & purging stainless steel pipe & tubing | Has high heat input, not popular in North America, globular |

# How to Calculate Filler Metal Consumption

The following tables will help you estimate electrode quantity and cost for a variety of joints. The bases for the tabulations are explained below.

Should you encounter a variation in conditions or joint preparation that is not shown in the tables, substitute appropriate figures in the W=D/(1-L) formula and calculate it.

Electrode requirements have been calculated as follows:

$$W = \frac{D}{1-L}$$

**W** = Weight of electrodes required

**D** = Weight of steel deposited

**L** = Total electrode losses

To arrive at the weight of steel deposited, it is necessary to calculate first the volume of deposited metal (area of the groove multiplied by the length). Then this volumetric value is converted to weight by the factor 0.283 pounds per cubic inch for steel. Where weld reinforcement is involved, it is added to the requirements for net, unreinforced welds.

These figures are based on the efficiency of the process used. On square and V-groove joints, the figures are based on stick electrode efficiency. For tubular wire results, divide steel deposit weight by .80, and for solid wire, divide by .90.

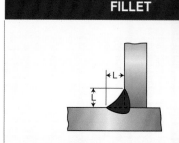

**HORIZONTAL FILLET**

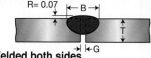

**SQUARE GROOVE BUTT JOINTS**

**...Welded one side**

R= 0.07

**...Welded both sides**

If root of top weld is chipped or flame gouged and welded, add 0.07 lb. to steel deposited (equivalent to approx. 0.13 lb. of electrodes).

R= 0.07

R= 0.07

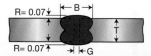

**V-GROOVE BUTT JOINT**

R= 0.08

60°

1/8

| Size of Fillet L (inches) | Pounds of Electrodes required per linear foot of weld* (Approximate) | Pounds of steel deposited per linear foot of weld |
|---|---|---|
| 1/8 | 0.048 | 0.027 |
| 3/16 | 0.113 | 0.063 |
| 1/4 | 0.189 | 0.106 |
| 5/16 | 0.296 | 0.166 |
| 3/8 | 0.427 | 0.239 |
| 1/2 | 0.760 | 0.425 |
| 5/8 | 1.185 | 0.663 |
| 3/4 | 1.705 | 0.955 |
| 1 | 3.030 | 1.698 |

| Joint Dimensions (inches) | | | Pounds of Electrodes required per linear foot of weld* (Approximate) | | Pounds of steel deposited per linear foot of weld | |
|---|---|---|---|---|---|---|
| Matl. Thick T | Bead Width B | Root Open O | Without Reinforcement | With Reinforcement | Without Reinforcement | With Reinforcement |
| 3/16 | 3/8 | 0 | – | 0.16 | – | 0.088 |
| 3/16 | 3/8 | 1/16 | 0.04 | 0.20 | 0.020 | 0.109 |
| 1/4 | 7/16 | 1/16 | 0.05 | 0.23 | 0.027 | 0.129 |
| 1/4 | 7/16 | 3/32 | 0.07 | 0.26 | 0.039 | 0.143 |
| 5/16 | 1/2 | 1/16 | 0.06 | 0.27 | 0.033 | 0.153 |
| 5/16 | 1/2 | 3/32 | 0.09 | 0.30 | 0.050 | 0.170 |
| 1/8 | 1/4 | 0 | – | 0.21 | – | 0.119 |
| 1/8 | 1/4 | 1/32 | 0.03 | 0.24 | 0.013 | 0.132 |
| 3/16 | 3/8 | 1/32 | 0.04 | 0.36 | 0.020 | 0.199 |
| 3/16 | 3/8 | 1/16 | 0.07 | 0.39 | 0.040 | 0.218 |
| 1/4 | 7/16 | 1/16 | 0.10 | 0.47 | 0.053 | 0.261 |
| 1/4 | 7/16 | 3/32 | 0.14 | 0.53 | 0.080 | 0.288 |

| Joint Dimensions (inches) | | | Pounds of Electrodes required per linear foot of weld* (Approximate) | | Pounds of steel deposited per linear foot of weld | |
|---|---|---|---|---|---|---|
| Matl. Thick T | Bead Width B | Root Open O | Without Reinforcement | With Reinforcement | Without Reinforcement | With Reinforcement |
| 1/4 | 0.207 | 1/16 | 0.15 | 0.25 | 0.085 | 0.143 |
| 5/16 | 0.311 | 3/32 | 0.31 | 0.46 | 0.173 | 0.258 |
| 3/8 | 0.414 | 1/8 | 0.50 | 0.70 | 0.282 | 0.394 |
| 1/2 | 0.558 | 1/8 | 0.87 | 1.15 | 0.489 | 0.641 |
| 3/4 | 0.702 | 1/8 | 1.35 | 1.68 | 0.753 | 0.942 |
| 3/4 | 0.847 | 1/8 | 1.94 | 2.35 | 1.088 | 1.320 |
| 0.81 | 1.138 | 1/8 | 13.45 | 4.00 | 1.930 | 2.240 |

# How AWS classifies mild steel covered electrodes – SMAW process

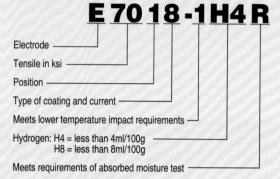

**E 70 18 -1 H4 R**

Electrode
Tensile in ksi
Position
Type of coating and current
Meets lower temperature impact requirements
Hydrogen: H4 = less than 4ml/100g
　　　　　 H8 = less than 8ml/100g
Meets requirements of absorbed moisture test

## Position

| | |
|---|---|
| 1 | Flat, Horizontal, Vertical, Overhead |
| 2 | Flat and Horizontal only |
| 4 | Flat, Horizontal, Vertical Down, Overhead |

## Type of coating and current

| Digit | Type of coating | Welding Current |
|---|---|---|
| 0 | Cellulose sodium | DCEP |
| 1 | Cellulose potassium | AC or DCEP |
| 2 | Titania sodium | AC or DCEN |
| 3 | titania potassium | AC or DCEP or DCEN |
| 4 | iron powder titania | AC or DCEN or DCEP |
| 5 | low hydrogen sodium | DCEP |
| 6 | low hydrogen potassium | AC or DCEP |
| 7 | iron powder iron oxide | AC or DCEP or DCEN |
| 8 | iron powder low hydrogen | AC or DCEP |
| E6020 | iron oxide sodium | AC or DCEP or DCEN |

DCEP — Direct Current Electrode Positive
DCEN — Direct Current Electrode Negative

# How AWS classifies low alloy covered electrodes

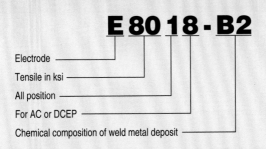

# E 80 1 8 - B2

Electrode
Tensile in ksi
All position
For AC or DCEP
Chemical composition of weld metal deposit

## Chemical composition of weld deposit

| Suffix | C | Mn | Si | Ni | Cr | Mo | Va |
|--------|------|-----------|---------|-----------|------------|----------|---------|
| A1 | .12 | .40 -.65* | .40-.80 | — | — | .40-.65 | — |
| B1 | .12 | .90 | .60-.80 | — | .40-.65 | .40-.65 | — |
| B2L | .05 | .90 | .8-1.00* | — | 1.00-1.50 | .40-.65 | — |
| B2 | .12 | .90 | .60-.90 | — | 1.00-1.50 | .40-.65 | — |
| B3L | .05 | .90 | .8-1.00* | — | 2.00-2.50 | .90-1.20 | — |
| B3 | .12 | .90 | .60-.80* | — | 2.00-2.50 | .90-1.20 | — |
| B4L | .05 | .90 | 1.00 | — | 1.75-2.25 | .40-.65 | — |
| B9 | .08-.13 | 1.25 | .30 | 1.0 | 8.00-10.50 | .85-1.2 | .15-.30 |
| C1 | .12 | 1.20 | .60-.80* | 1.00-2.75 | — | — | — |
| C2 | .12 | 1.20 | —* | 3.00-3.75 | — | — | — |
| C3 | .12 | .40-1.25 | .80 | .80-1.10 | .15 | .35 | .05 |
| D1 | .12 | 1.25-1.75 | .60-.80* | — | — | .25-.45 | — |
| D2 | .15 | 1.65-2.00 | .6-.8* | — | — | .25-.45 | — |
| G | — | 1.0 Min | .80 Min | .50 Min | .30 Min | .20 Min | .10 M |
| M** | .10 | .60-2.25* | .60-.80* | 1.40-2.50* | .15-1.50* | .25-55* | .05 |

\* Amount depends on electrode classification. Single values indicate maximum, refer to AWS 5.5 for the different electrode classes.

\*\* There are several different M classes. M classifications are intended to conform to military specifications.

## Pieces per pound arc welding electrodes

| Hobart Type | Diameter | 3/32" | 3/32" | 1/8" | 5/32" | 3/16" | 3/16" | 1/4" |
|---|---|---|---|---|---|---|---|---|
| | Length | 10" | 14" | 14" | 14" | 14" | 18" | 18" |
| Pipemaster 60, 70, 80 | | — | 30 | 17 | 12 | 8 | — | — |
| 335A | | — | 29 | 16 | 11 | 7 | — | — |
| 447A | | — | 30 | 15 | 10 | 7 | — | — |
| 14A | | — | 23 | 13 | 9 | 6 | — | — |
| 24 (-1) | | — | — | 10 | 7 | — | 4 | 2 |
| XX18 (Iron Powder) | | — | 21 | 12 | 9 | 7 | — | 3 |
| Stainless | | 22 | — | 13 | 9 | 4 | — | 3 |

## Comparative index of mild steel & low hydrogen electrodes

| AWS Class | HOBART | MUREX | ESAB | LINCOLN |
|---|---|---|---|---|
| E6010 | Pipemaster Pro-60 Hobart 610 | – | SW-10P; SW-10P Plus | Fleetweld 5P, 5P+; Pipeliner 6P+ |
| E6011 | 335A | 6011C | SW-14 | Fleetweld 35; 35LS; 180 |
| E6013 | 447A | 6013D | SW-15; 6013LV | Fleetweld 37 |
| E6022 | 1139 | – | – | Fleetweld 22 |
| E7010-P1 | Pipemaster 70 | – | 710P | Shield-Arc HYP+ Pipeliner 7P+ |
| E7014 | 14A | 7014 | SW-15 IP | Fleetweld 47 |
| E7018 (AC) | 18AC | – | Atom Arc 7018-AC | Lincoln 7018AC |
| E7018 | 418; 718MC 7018 XLM | 7018MR | Atom Arc 7018 | Excalibur 7018MR; Jetweld LH-70; Jet-LH-78 MR |
| E7018-1 | 418; 718MC 7018 XLM | – | Atom Arc 7018-1 | Excalibur 7018-1MR |
| E7024 E7024-1 | 24 | 7024 – | Sureweld 7024 Sureweld 7024 | Jetweld 1 |
| E8010-P1 | Pipemaster 80 | – | SW-810P | Pipeliner 8P+ Shield-Arc 80 |
| E9010-G | Pipemaster 90 | – | – | Shield-Arc 90 |

| Comparative index of low alloy electrodes | | | |
|---|---|---|---|
| AWS Class | HOBART | ESAB | LINCOLN |
| 7018-A1 | Hoballoy 7018A1 | Atom Arc 7018-Mo | Excalibur 7018-A1 MR |
| E8018-B2 | Hoballoy 8018-B2 | Atom Arc 8018-CM | – |
| E8018-C1 | Hoballoy 8018C1 | Atom Arc 8018-C1 | Excalibur 8018-C1 MR |
| E8018-C3 | Hoballoy 8018C3 | Atom Arc 8018 | Excalibur 8018-C3 MR |
| E9018-B3 | Hoballoy 9018B3 | Atom Arc 9018-CM | – |
| E9018M | Hoballoy 9018M | Atom Arc 9018 | Excalibur 9018M MR |
| E10018-D2 | Hoballoy 10018D2 | Atom Arc 10018-MM | – |
| E10018M | Hoballoy 10018M | Atom Arc T | Excalibur 11018 MR |
| E12018M | Hoballoy 12018M | Atom Arc 12018 | – |

# How AWS classifies stainless steel coated electrodes – SMAW process

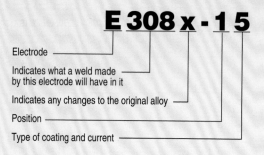

# E 308 x - 1 5

Electrode

Indicates what a weld made by this electrode will have in it

Indicates any changes to the original alloy

Position

Type of coating and current

## Additional Requirements

| Suffix | Changes made or additional requirements |
|---|---|
| L | Has a lower carbon content |
| H | Limited to the upper range on the carbon content |
| Mo | Molybdenum added – pitting resistance, creep strength, ferrite increased |
| Cb (Nb) | Columbium added – prevents corrosion just outside of the weld bead |
| LR | Low Residuals – lower range for: C, Si, P, S – narrower range: Cb and Mn |

| Dash number | Out of Position | Bead Ripple | Slag Removal | Spatter Level | Transfer Type | Operating Current | Bead Profile |
|---|---|---|---|---|---|---|---|
| -x5 | 1 (5/32") | 3 | 3 | 3 | Globular | DCEP | Convex |
| -x6 | 2 (5/32") | 2 | 2 | 2 | Globular | AC/DCEP | Flat |
| -x7 | 3 (3/16") | 1 | 1 | 1 | Spray | AC/DCEP | Concave |

Ratings: 1 = the best, 3 = the least

Note: Nb (Niobium) is the European name for Columbium.

# How AWS classifies stainless steel flux-cored wires

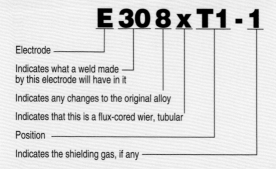

**E 30 8 x T1 - 1**

Electrode

Indicates what a weld made by this electrode will have in it

Indicates any changes to the original alloy

Indicates that this is a flux-cored wier, tubular

Position

Indicates the shielding gas, if any

## Shielding Chart

| Dash number | Shielding Gas | Welding Current |
|---|---|---|
| -1 | $CO_2$ | DCEP |
| -3 | None | DCEP |
| -4 | 75% Ar/25% $CO_2$ | DCEP |

## Additional Requirements

| Suffix | Changes made or additional requirements |
|---|---|
| L | Has a lower carbon content |
| H | Limited to the upper range on the carbon content |
| Mo | Molybdenum added – pitting resistance, creep strength, ferrite increased |
| Cb (Nb) | Columbium added – prevents corrosion just outside of the weld bead |
| Ni | Nickel added – high temperature strength, corrosion resistance, added toughness |
| Ti | Titanium added – prevents corrosion just outside of the weld bead |
| K | Specially formulated for cryogenic temperature service (less than -238°F) |

Note: Nb (Niobium) is the European name for Columbium.

## Stainless electrodes for AISI steels

| AISI Number | Chemical Analyses of Stainless Steels (percent) | | | | | | Weld With Type |
|---|---|---|---|---|---|---|---|
| | Carbon | Manganese | Silicon | Chromium | Nickel | Other Elements | |
| 201 | 0.15 max. | 5.5-7.5 | 1.0 | 16.0-18.0 | 3.5-5.5 | $N_2$ 0.25 max. | 308 |
| 202 | 0.15 max. | 7.5-10. | 1.0 | 17.0-19.0 | 4.0-6.0 | $N_2$ 0.25 max. | 308 |
| 301 | 0.15 max. | 2.0 | 1.0 | 16.0-18.0 | 6.0-8.0 | – | 308 |
| 302 | 0.15 max. | 2.0 | 1.0 | 17.0-19.0 | 8.0-10.0 | – | 308, 309 |
| 302B | 0.15 max. | 2.0 | 2.0-3.0 | 17.0-19.0 | 8.0-10.0 | – | 308 |
| 303 | 0.15 max. | 2.0 | 1.0 | 17.0-19.0 | 8.0-10.0 | S 0.15 min. | 312* |
| 303Se | 0.15 max. | 2.0 | 1.0 | 17.0-19.0 | 8.0-10.0 | Se 0.15 min. | 308 |
| 304 | 0.08 max. | 2.0 | 1.0 | 18.0-20.0 | 8.0-10.0 | – | 308L, 347 |
| 304L | 0.03 max. | 2.0 | 1.0 | 18.0-20.0 | 8.0-10.0 | – | 308 |
| 305 | 0.12 max. | 2.0 | 1.0 | 17.0-19.0 | 10.0-13.0 | – | 308 |
| 308 | 0.08 max. | 2.0 | 1.0 | 19.0-21.0 | 10.0-12.0 | – | 309 |
| 309 | 0.20 max. | 2.0 | 1.0 | 22.0-24.0 | 12.0-15.0 | – | 309 |
| 309S | 0.08 max. | 2.0 | 1.0 | 22.0-24.0 | 12.0-15.0 | – | 310. 309 |
| 310 | 0.25 max. | 2.0 | 1.0 | 24.0-26.0 | 19.0-22.0 | – | 310 |
| 310S | 0.08 max. | 2.0 | 1.50 | 24.0-26.0 | 19.0-22.0 | – | 310 |
| 314 | 0.25 max. | 2.0 | 1.50 | 23.0-26.0 | 19.0-22.0 | – | 316, 316Mo |
| 316 | 0.08 max. | 2.0 | 1.5-3.0 | 16.0-18.0 | 10.0-14.0 | Mo 2.0-3.0 | 316L |
| 316L | 0.03 max. | 2.0 | 1.0 | 16.0-18.0 | 10.0-14.0 | Mo 2.0-3.0 | 317 |
| 317 | 0.08 max. | 2.0 | 1.0 | 18.0-20.0 | 11.0-15.0 | Mo 3.0-4.0 | 317L |
| 321 | 0.08 max. | 2.0 | 1.0 | 17.0-19.0 | 9.0-12.0 | Ti 5xC min. | 321, 347 |
| 347 | 0.08 max. | 2.0 | 1.0 | 17.0-19.0 | 9.0-13.0 | Cb + Ta 10xC min. | 347, 308L |
| 348 | 0.08 max. | 2.0 | 1.0 | 17.0-19.0 | 9.0-13.0 | Ta 0.10 max. | 347 |

*Courtesy of the American Iron and Steel Institute.*

## Comparative index of stainless steel electrodes

| AWS Class | McKay | Techalloy | Sandvik | Lincoln |
|-----------|-------|-----------|---------|---------|
| E308L-16 | 308/308L Sterling AP | Tech Rod 308L-16 | – | Red Baron 308L MR |
| E308H-16 | 308/308H Sterling AP | Tech Rod 308-16 | – | Red Baron 308/308H MR |
| E309L-16 | 309/309L Sterling AP | Tech Rod 309L-16 | – | Red Baron 309/309L MR |
| E310-16 | 310 AC-DC | Tech Rod 310-16 | – | Red Baron 310 MR |
| E312-16 | 312 AC-DC | Tech Rod 312-16 | 29.9 R | – |
| E316L-16 | 316/316L Sterling AP | Tech Rod 316L-16 | 19.12.3. LRV | Red Baron 316/316L MR |
| E316H-16 | 316/316H Sterling AP | Tech Rod 316-16 | – | – |
| E317L-16 | 317L AC-DC | Tech Rod 317-16 | 19.13.4. LR | – |
| E347-16 | 347 AC-DC | Tech Rod 347-16 | – | – |
| E2209-16 | 2209 AC-DC | Tech Rod 2209 | 22.9.3. LR (B) | – |

# How AWS classifies mild steel solid electrodes – GMAW, GTAW and PAW

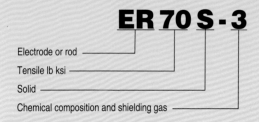

## ER 70 S - 3

- Electrode or rod ————————
- Tensile lb ksi ————————
- Solid ————————
- Chemical composition and shielding gas ————————

## Position of welding, shielding, polarity, and application requirements

| AWS Classification | Shielding Gas | Yield Strength KSi (MPa) | Tensile Strength KSi (MPa) | % Elongation Min. in 2" (50mm) | Impact Strength Min. ft-lbs at ºF (J at ºC) |
|---|---|---|---|---|---|
| ER70S-2 | CO$_2$ | 72 (500) | 60 (420) | 22 | 20 at -20 (27 at -29) |
| ER70S-3 | CO$_2$ | 72 (500) | 60 (420) | 22 | 20 at 0 (27 at -18) |
| ER70S-4 | CO$_2$ | 72 (500) | 60 (420) | 22 | — |
| ER70S-5 | CO$_2$ | 72 (500) | 60 (420) | 22 | — |
| ER70S-6 | CO$_2$ | 72 (500) | 60 (420) | 22 | 20 at -20 (27 at -29) |
| ER70S-7 | CO$_2$ | 72 (500) | 60 (420) | 22 | 20 at -20 (27 at -29) |
| ER80S-D2 | CO$_2$ | 80 (550) | 68 (470) | 17 | 20 at -20 (27 at -29) |

## Chemical Composition

| C | Mn | Si | P | S | Ni | Cr | Mo | Cu | Other |
|---|---|---|---|---|---|---|---|---|---|
| .07 | .90-1.40 | .40-.70 | .025 | .035 | — | — | — | .50 | Ti, Zr, Al |
| 06-.15 | .90-1.40 | .40-.70 | .025 | .035 | — | — | — | .50 | — |
| .07-.15 | 1.00-1.50. | 65-.85 | .025 | .035 | — | — | — | .50 | — |
| .07-.19 | .90-1.40 | .30-.60 | .025 | .035 | — | — | — | .50 | Al |
| .07-.15 | 1.40-1.85 | .80-.1.15 | .025 | .035 | — | — | — | .50 | — |
| .07-.15 | 1.50-2.00 | .50-.80 | .025 | .035 | — | — | — | .50 | — |
| .07-.12 | 1.60-2.10 | .50-.80 | .025 | .025 | .15 | — | .40-.60 | .50 | — |

# How AWS classifies metal-cored wires – GMAW process (AWS A5.18)

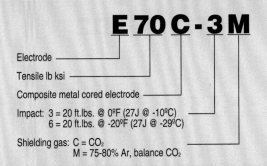

**E 70 C - 3 M**

Electrode

Tensile lb ksi

Composite metal cored electrode

Impact: 3 = 20 ft.lbs. @ 0°F (27J @ -10°C)
6 = 20 ft.lbs. @ -20°F (27J @ -29°C)

Shielding gas: C = $CO_2$
M = 75-80% Ar, balance $CO_2$

## Position of welding, shielding, polarity, and application requirements

| AWS Classification | Welding Position[a] | Shielding[b] | Current[c] | Application[d] |
|---|---|---|---|---|
| E70C-3X | F and H | 75-80% Ar/Balance $CO_2$ or 100% $CO_2$ | DCEP | M |
| E70C-6X | F and H | 75-80% Ar/Balance $CO_2$ or 100% $CO_2$ | DCEP | M |
| E70C-G(X) | F and H | (f) | DCEP | M |
| E70C-GS(X) | F and H | (f) | DCEP | S |

## Chemical Composition Requirements for Weld Metal from Composite Electrodes

| C | Mn | Si | S | P | Ni | Cr | Mo | V | Cu |
|---|---|---|---|---|---|---|---|---|---|
| 0.12 | 1.75 | 0.90 | 0.03 | 0.03 | (e) | (e) | (e) | (e) | 0.50 |
| 0.12 | 1.75 | 0.90 | 0.03 | 0.03 | (e) | (e) | (e) | (e) | 0.50 |

Not Specified for -G[g]

Chemical Requirements not specified for -GS[h]

**Notes:**
a. The final X shown in the classification represents a "C" or "M" which corresponds to the shielding gas with which the electrode is classified. The use of "C" designates 100% $CO_2$ shielding, "M" designates 75-80% Ar/balance $CO_2$. For E70C-G and E70C-GS, the final "C" or "M" may be omitted if these gases are not used for classification.
b. F = Flat, H = Horizontal.
c. Use of a shielding gas other than that specified will result in different weld metal composition.
d. Single values are maximum weight percent.
e. To be reported if intentionally added; the sum of Ni, Cr, Mo, and V shall not exceed 0.50%.
f. Shielding gas shall be as agreed upon between purchaser and supplier.
g. Composition shall be reported; the requirements are those agreed to between purchaser and supplier.
h. The composition of weld metal from this classification is not specified since electrodes of this classification are intended only for single pass welds. Dilution, in such welds, usually is quite high.

# How AWS classifies low alloy solid electrodes – GMAW, GTAW, and PAW

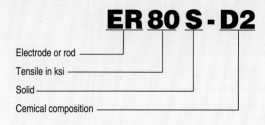

**ER 80 S - D2**

Electrode or rod ——————
Tensile in ksi ——————
Solid ——————
Cemical composition ——————

## Typical shielding gas mixtures and their uses

| Type of Gas | Typical Mixtures | Primary Uses |
|---|---|---|
| Argon | | Non-ferrous Metals |
| Helium | | Aluminum, Magnesium, and Copper Alloys |
| Carbon Dioxide | | Mild and Low Alloy |
| Argon-Helium | 20-80% He | Aluminum, Magnesium, Copper and Nickel Alloys |
| Argon-Oxygen | 1-2% $O_2$ | Stainless Steel |
| | 3-5 $O_2$ | Mild and Low Alloy |
| Argon-Cabon Dioxide | 20-50% $CO_2$ | Mild and Low Alloy Steel |
| Helium-Argon-Carbon Dioxide | 90He-7-1/2A-2-1/2 $CO_2$ | Stainless Steel |
| | 60-7He-25-36Ar-5 $CO_2$ | Low Alloy Steels |
| Nitrogen | | Copper Alloys |

## Short circuit transfer welding parameters

| Material thickness | | | Electrode Diameter | | Welding current amps - DC | Arc voltage (electrode positive) | Wire feed speed ipm | Travel speed ipm | Shielding gas flow CFH[2] |
|---|---|---|---|---|---|---|---|---|---|
| Size | In. (decimal) | mm | in. | mm | | | | | |
| 24 ga. | 0.025 | 0.6 | 0.024 | 0.6 | 30-50 | 15-17 | 85-100 | 12-20 | 15-20 |
| 22 ga. | 0.031 | 0.8 | 0.030 | 0.8 | 40-60 | 15-17 | 90-130 | 18-22 | 15-20 |
| 20 ga. | 0.037 | 0.9 | 0.035 | 0.9 | 55-85 | 15-17 | 70-120 | 35-40 | 15-20 |
| 18 ga. | 0.050 | 1.3 | 0.035 | 0.9 | 70-100 | 16-19 | 100-160 | 35-40 | 15-20 |
| 1/16" | 0.063 | 1.6 | 0.035 | 0.9 | 80-110 | 17-20 | 120-180 | 30-35 | 20-25 |
| 5/64" | 0.078 | 2.0 | 0.035 | 0.9 | 100-130 | 18-20 | 160-220 | 25-30 | 20-25 |
| 1/8" | 0.125 | 3.2 | 0.035 | 0.9 | 120-160 | 19-22 | 210-290 | 20-25 | 20-25 |
| 1/8" | 0.125 | 3.2 | 0.045 | 1.1 | 180-200 | 20-24 | 210-240 | 27-32 | 20-25 |
| 3/16" | 0.187 | 4.7 | 0.035 | 0.9 | 140-160 | 19-22 | 210-290 | 14-19 | 20-25 |
| 3/16" | 0.187 | 4.7 | 0.045 | 1.1 | 180-205 | 20-24 | 210-245 | 18-22 | 20-25 |
| 1/4" | 0.250 | 6.4 | 0.035 | 0.9 | 140-160 | 19-22 | 240-290 | 11-15 | 20-25 |
| 1/4" | 0.250 | 6.4 | 0.045 | 1.1 | 180-225 | 20-24 | 210-290 | 12-18 | 20-25 |

Note: Single-pass flat and horizontal fillet positions. Reduce current 10 to 15% for vertical and overhead welding.
1. For fillet and groove welds – for fillet welds, size equals metal thickness; for square groove welds, the root opening should equal 1/2 the metal thickness.
2. Shielding gas is $CO_2$, or 75% Ar/25% $CO_2$.

## Shielding gases for GMAW short circuiting transfer

| Metal | Shielding gas / advantage |
|---|---|
| Carbon steel | $CO_2$ — Broad penetration; reduces chances of porosity. |
| | Ar/25% $CO_2$ — High welding speeds without burn-through; minimum distortion and spatter. |
| | Ar/5-10% $CO_2$ — Deeper penetration; faster welding speeds. |
| Low alloy steel | 60-70% He/25-35% Ar/4-5% $CO_2$ — Minimum reactivity; excellent toughness; excellent arc stability, wetting characteristics, and bead contour; little spatter. |
| | 75% Ar/25% $CO_2$ — Fair toughness; excellent arc stability, wetting characteristics and bead contour; little spatter. |

## Spray transfer welding parameters

| Material thickness | | | Type of weld[1] | Electrode Diameter | | Welding current amps - DC | Arc voltage (electrode positive) | Wire feed speed ipm | Travel speed ipm | Shielding gas flow CFH[2] |
|---|---|---|---|---|---|---|---|---|---|---|
| Size | In. (dec.) | mm | | in. | mm | | | | | |
| 18 ga. | 0.050 | 1.3 | fillet | 0.045 | 1.1 | 280 | 26 | 350 | 190 | 25 |
| 16 ga. | 0.063 | 1.6 | fillet | 0.045 | 1.1 | 325 | 26 | 360 | 150 | 35 |
| | | | square groove | 0.045 | 1.1 | 300 | 28 | 350 | 140 | 35 |
| 14 ga. | 0.078 | 2.0 | fillet | 0.045 | 1.1 | 325 | 27 | 360 | 130 | 35 |
| | | | square groove | 0.045 | 1.1 | 325 | 29 | 360 | 110 | 35 |
| | | | square groove | 0.045 | 1.1 | 330 | 29 | 350 | 105 | 35 |
| 11 ga. | 0.125 | 3.2 | fillet | 1/16 | 1.6 | 380 | 28 | 210 | 85 | 35 |
| | | | square groove | 0.045 | 1.1 | 350 | 29 | 380 | 100 | 35 |
| 3/16" | 0.188 | 4.8 | fillet | 1/16 | 1.6 | 425 | 31 | 260 | 75 | 35 |
| | | | square groove | 1/16 | 1.6 | 425 | 30 | 320 | 76 | 35 |
| | | | square groove | 1/16 | 1.6 | 375 | 31 | 260 | 70 | 35 |
| 1/4" | 0.250 | 6.4 | square groove | 1/16 | 1.6 | 475 | 32 | 340 | 55 | 35 |

1. For mild carbon and low alloy steels – on square groove welds, backing is required.

## Shielding gases for GMAW spray transfer

| Metal | Shielding gas / advantage |
|---|---|
| Carbon steel | **95-98% Ar/2-5% $O_2$** — Improves arc stability; produces a more fluid and controllable puddle; good coalescence and bead contour; minimizes undercutting; permits higher speeds than pure argon. |
| | **90-92% Ar/8-10% $CO_2$** — High-speed mechanized welding; low-cost manual welding; pulsed welding. |
| Low alloy steel | **90-92% Ar/8-10% $CO_2$** — High-speed mechanized welding; low-cost manual welding; pulsed welding. |

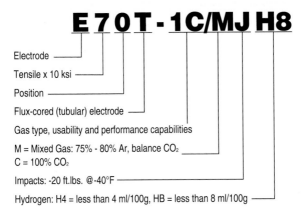

**E 7 0 T - 1 C/M J H8**

Electrode ─────┘

Tensile x 10 ksi ──────┘

Position ────────┘

Flux-cored (tublular) electrode ─────────┘

Gas type, usability and performance capabilities

M = Mixed Gas: 75% - 80% Ar, balance $CO_2$ ────────┘

C = 100% $CO_2$

Impacts: -20 ft.lbs. @-40°F ────────────┘

Hydrogen: H4 = less than 4 ml/100g, HB = less than 8 ml/100g ──────────┘

**a. H** = horizontal position
  **F** = flat position
  **OH** = overhead position
  **VD** = vertical position with downward progression
  **VU** = vertical position with upward progression

*Footnotes for Table next page.*

**b.** Properties of weld metal from electrodes that are used with external gas shielding (EXXT-1, EXXT-1M, EXXT-2, EXXT-2M, EXXT-5, EXXT-5M, EXXT-9, EXXT-9M, EXXT-12, and EXXT-12M) vary according to the shielding gas employed. Electrodes classified with the specified shielding gas should not be used with other shielding gases without first consulting the manufacturer of the electrode.

**c.** The term "DCEP" refers to direct current electrode positive (DC, reverse polarity). The term "DCEN" refers to direct current electrode negative (DC, straight polarity).

**d. M** = single- or multiple-pass
  **S** = single-pass only

**e.** Some E71T-5 and E71T-5M electrodes may be recommended for use on DCEN for improved out-of-position welding.

| AWS Classification | Welding Position[a] | Shielding[b] | Current[c] | Application[d] |
|---|---|---|---|---|
| E70T-1 | H and F | $CO_2$ | DCEP | M |
| E70T-1M | H and F | 75-80% Ar/bal $CO_2$ | DCEP | M |
| E71T-1 | H, F, VU, OH | $CO_2$ | DCEP | M |
| E71T-1M | H, F, VU, OH | 75-80% Ar/bal $CO_2$ | DCEP | M |
| E70T-2 | H and F | $CO_2$ | DCEP | S |
| E70T-2M | H and F | 75-80% Ar/bal $CO_2$ | DCEP | S |
| E71T-2 | H, F, VU, OH | $CO_2$ | DCEP | S |
| E71T-2M | H, F, VU, OH | 75-80% Ar/bal $CO_2$ | DCEP | S |
| E70T-3 | H and F | None | DCEP | S |
| E70T-4 | H and F | None | DCEP | M |
| E70T-5 | H and F | $CO_2$ | DCEP | M |
| E70T-5M | H and F | 75-80% Ar/bal $CO_2$ | DCEP | M |
| E71T-5 | H, F, VU, OH | $CO_2$ | DCEP or DCEN[e] | M |
| E71T-5M | H, F, VU, OH | 75-80% Ar/bal $CO_2$ | DCEP or DCEN[e] | M |
| E70T-6 | H and F | None | DCEP | M |
| E70T-7 | H and F | None | DCEN | M |
| E71T-7 | H, F, VU, OH | None | DCEN | M |
| E70T-8 | H and F | None | DCEN | M |
| E71T-8 | H, F, VU, OH | None | DCEN | M |
| E70T-9 | H and F | CO2 | DCEP | M |
| E70T-9M | H and F | 75-80% Ar/bal $CO_2$ | DCEP | M |
| E71T-9 | H, F, VU, OH | $CO_2$ | DCEP | M |
| E71T-9M | H, F, VU, OH | 75-80% Ar/bal $CO_2$ | DCEP | M |
| E70T-10 | H and F | None | DCEN | S |
| E70T-11 | H and F | None | DCEN | M |
| E71T-11 | H, F, VD, OH | None | DCEN | M |
| E70T-12 | H and F | $CO_2$ | DCEP | M |
| E70T-12M | H and F | 75-80% Ar/bal $CO_2$ | DCEP | M |
| E71T-12 | H, F, VU, OH | $CO_2$ | DCEP | M |
| E71T-12M | H, F, VU, OH | 75-80% Ar/bal $CO_2$ | DCEP | M |
| E61T-13 | H, F, VD, OH | None | DCEN | S |
| E71T-13 | H, F, VD, OH | None | DCEN | S |
| E71T-14 | H, F, VD, OH | None | DCEN | S |
| EX0T-G | H and F | Not Specified | Not Specified | M |
| EX1T-G | H, F, VD or VU, OH | Not Specified | Not Specified | M |
| EX0T-GS | H and F | Not Specified | Not Specified | S |
| EX1T-GS | H, F, VD or VU, OH | Not Specified | Not Specified | S |

## Comparative index of self-shielded tubular wires

| AWS Class | HOBART | Corex | ESAB | LINCOLN | Select Arc |
|-----------|--------|-------|------|---------|------------|
| E70T-4 | FABSHIELD 4 | Self-Shield 4 | Coreshield 40 | Innershield NS-3M | Select 74 |
| E70T-7 | FABSHIELD 7027 | Self-Shield 7 | Coreshield 7 | Innershield NR-311 | – |
| E71T-11 | FABSHIELD 21B | Self-Shield 11 | Coreshield 11 | Innershield NR-211-MP | Select 701 |
| E71T-8 | FABSHIELD XLR-8 | – | Coreshield 8 | Innershield MR-232, NR-233 | – |

## Comparative index of gas-shielded tubular wires

| AWS Class | HOBART | ESAB | LINCOLN | Select Arc |
|-----------|--------|------|---------|------------|
| E70C-6M | FabCOR 86R | Coreweld 70, Coreweld Ultra | MC-710, MC-6 | Select 70C-3, C-6 |
| E70T-1C E70T-9C | FabCO RXR FabCO TR-70 | Dual Shield 111 AC, R-70 Ultra | Outershield 70 Outershield HD70 | Select 79 Select 70 |
| E70T-5C | FabCO 85 | Dual Shield T-75 | Outershield 71, 71M, Elite | – |
| E71T-1C (CO$_2$) E71T-9C | EXCEL-ARC 71 | Dual Shield 7100 Ultra Dual Shield II 71 Ultra | Outershield 75-H | Select 712 |
| E71T-1M, E71T-9M (75% Ar/25% CO$_2$) | EXCEL-ARC 71 | Dual Shield 7000 Dual Shield 7100 Ultra | Outershield 71, 71M, Elite | Select 710 |
| E71T-1C (CO2) E71T-12CJ | Formula XL-550 | Dual Shield II-71 Ultra | Outershield 71C-H, Elite | Select 720 |
| E71T-1M (75% Ar/25% CO$_2$) 71T-12MJ | Formula XL-525 | Dual Shield II-70 Ultra Dual Shield II-70T12 | Outershield 71M-H, Elite | Select 720 |
| E81T1-Ni1MJ | Formula XL-8Ni1 | Dual Shield II 80-Ni1 Dual Shield 8000C3 | Outershield 81Ni1-H | – |
| E81T1-K2C | FabCO 81K2-C | Dual Shield II 81K2 | Outershield 81K2-H | Select 812-K2 |
| E91T1-K2C | FabCO 91K2-C | Dual Shield II 9100K2 | Outershield 91K2-H | Select 910-K2 |
| E110T5-K4C | FabCO 115 | Dual Shield T-115 | – | |

# Hobart Filler Metals

The information contained or otherwise referenced herein is presented only as "typical" without guarantee or warranty, and Hobart Brothers Company expressly disclaims any liability incurred from any reliance theron. Typical data are those obtained when welded and tested in accordance with AWS specifications. Other tests and procedures may produce different results. No data is to be construed as a recommendation for any welding condition or technique not controlled by Hobart Brothers Company.

**Notice:**

Actual use of the products may produce varying results due to conditions and welding techniques over which the producer has no control, including, but not limited to, plate chemistry, weldment design, fabrication methods, electrode size, welding procedure, service requirements and environment. The purchaser is solely responsible for determining the suitability of any products for the purchaser's own use. Any prior representations shall not be binding. The companies disclaim any warranty of merchantability or fitness for any particular purpose with respect to its products.

**Caution:**

Consumers should be thoroughly familiar with the safety precautions shown on the Warning Label posted on each shipment in and in American National Standard Z49.1, "Safety in Welding and Cutting," published by the American Welding Society, 8669 NW36th St., #130, Miami, FL 33166, and OSHA Safety and Health Standards 29 CFR 1910, available from the U.S. Department of Labor, Washington, D.C. 20210.

## Pipemaster® Pro-60
AWS E6010

Pipemaster Pro-60 is a quick-starting, cellulosic mild steel electrode that provides you with outstanding arc stability, penetration and wash-in. It's ideal for welding in all positions and produces an X-ray quality weld with light slag that's easy to remove. Pipemaster Pro-60 can be used to weld the following API 5L steels: Grade A, B, X-42, X-46, X-52, X-56 and for the root pass on material up to X-80. It features enhanced weldabilty and increased physical properties. Earthtone grey coating.

**Typical applications:**
- Construction and shipbuilding
- General-purpose fabrication
- Maintenance welding
- Out-of-position X-ray welds
- Pipe welding
- Vertical and overhead plate welding

**Typical weld metal properties (Chem Pad):**
| | |
|---|---|
| Carbon | 0.13 |
| Manganese | 0.39 |
| Silicon | 0.14 |
| Chromium | 0.06 |
| Nickel | 0.08 |
| Molybdenum | <0.01 |
| Vanadium | 0.01 |

**Typical mechanical properties (AW):**
Tensile Strength (psi) .......79,000 (542 MPa)
Yield Strength (psi)............66,000 (456 MPa)
Elongation % in 2" .............23%

**Typical Charpy V-notch impact values (AW):**
Avg. at -20°F (-29°C) 48 ft.lb. (65J)

**Available diameter and recommended operating ranges:**
| | |
|---|---|
| 3/32" (2.4 mm) | 40-70 amps |
| 1/8" (3.2 mm) | 65-130 amps |
| 5/32" (4.0 mm) | 90-175 amps |
| 3/16" (4.8 mm) | 140-225 amps |

**Type of current:** DCEP

**Approvals and conformances:**
- AWS A5.1, E6010
- ASME SFA 5.1, E6010
- Lloyd's Grade 3m
- ABS E6010

## Hobart® 610
AWS E6010

Use Hobart 610 for quick starting, excellent arc stability, superior arc drive (penetration), light slag and excellent wash-in. An all-position cellulosic mild steel electrode, it outdoes itself in producing X-ray quality welds. Earthtone grey coating.

**Typical applications:**
- Construction and shipbuilding
- General-purpose fabrication
- Maintenance welding
- Out-of-position X-ray welds
- Pipe welding
- Vertical and overhead plate welding

**Typical weld metal properties (Chem Pad):**
| | |
|---|---|
| Carbon | 0.12 |
| Manganese | 0.52 |
| Silicon | 0.17 |
| Chromium | 0.04 |
| Nickel | 0.06 |
| Molybdenum | < 0.01 |
| Vanadium | 0.01 |

**Typical mechanical properties (AW):**
Tensile Strength (psi) ........84,000 (576 MPa)
Yield Strength (psi) ............70,000 (479 MPa)
Elongation % in 2" ............26%

**Typical Charpy V-notch impact values (AW):**
Avg. at -20°F (-29°C) 56 ft.lb. (76J)

**Available diameter and recommended operating ranges:**
3/32" (2.4 mm)...................40-70 amps
1/8" (3.2 mm).....................65-130 amps
5/32" (4.0 mm)...................90-175 amps
3/16" (4.8 mm ...................40-225 amps

**Type of current:** DCEP

**Approvals and conformances:**
- AWS A5.1, E6010
- ASME SFA 5.1, E6010
- CWB E4310

## Pipemaster® 70
AWS E7010-P1

The Pipemaster 70, an all-position cellulosic mild steel electrode, is excellent for producing X-ray quality welds. It's quick starting with excellent arc stability, superior penetration, light slag and excellent wash-in. Pipemaster 70 can also help you handle vertical-down welding on all passes on 5L, 5LX and X52 through X65 pipe.

**Typical applications:**
- Welding of high-yield pipe steels
- Pipeline welding using downhill travel
- Shipbuilding
- Storage tanks
- Drill platforms

**Typical weld metal properties (Chem Pad):**
| | |
|---|---|
| Carbon | 0.15 |
| Manganese | 0.54 |
| Silicon | 0.14 |
| Nickel | 0.72 |
| Molybdenum | < 0.01 |
| Phosphorus | 0.01 |
| Sulphur | 0.01 |
| Chromium | 0.02 |
| Vanadium | 0.01 |

**Typical mechanical properties (AW):**
Tensile Strength (psi) ........83,000 (570 MPa)
Yield Strength (psi) ............69,000 (475 MPa)
Elongation % in 2" ............25%

**Typical Charpy V-notch impact values (AW):**
Avg. at -20°F (-29°C) 57 ft.lb. (78J)

**Available diameter and recommended operating ranges:**
1/8" (3.2 mm).....................70-140 amps
5/32" (4.0 mm)...................80-190 amps
3/16" (4.8 mm)...................20-230 amps

**Type of current:** DCEP

**Approvals and conformances:**
- AWS A5.5, E7010-P1
- ASME SFA 5.5, E7010-P1
- Lloyd's Grade 3m, 3Ym
- ABS E7010-P1

*For more information: http://www.hobartbrothers.com*

## Pipemaster® 80
AWS E8010-P1

With features like quick starting, excellent arc stability, superior penetration, light slag and excellent wash-in, the Pipemaster 80 is great for a variety of jobs. This all-position cellulosic mild steel electrode gets a handle on vertical-down welding on all passes with X56 through X70 pipe. And with good low-temperature impact properties, it can be used on pipe steels with relatively high silicon (up to .30).

**Typical applications:**
• Welding of high-yield pipe steels
• Pipe welding using downhill travel
• Shipbuilding
• Storage tanks
• Drill platforms

**Typical weld metal properties (ChemPad):**
Carbon..........................................0.19
Manganese....................................0.84
Silicon..........................................0.25
Nickel...........................................0.87
Molybdenum..................................0.14
Phosphorus...................................0.008
Sulphur.........................................0.015
Chromium......................................0.07
Vanadium......................................0.01

**Typical mechanical properties (AW):**
Tensile Strength (psi) ........98,000 (672 MPa)
Yield Strength (psi)............81,000 (560 MPa)
Elongation % in 2"..............19%

**Typical Charpy V-notch impact values (AW):**
Avg. at -20°F (-29°C) 42 ft.lb. (57J)

**Available diameter and recommended operating ranges:**
1/8" (3.2 mm).....................70-140 amps
5/32" (4.0 mm)....................80-190 amps
3/16" (4.8 mm).................130-240 amps

**Type of current:** DCEP

**Approvals and conformances:**
• AWS A5.5, E8010-P1
• ASME SFA 5.5, E8010-P1
• Lloyd's Grade 3m, 3Ym
• ABS E8010-P1

## Hobart® 335A
AWS E6011

The Hobart 335A offers a fine spray transfer that enhances operator appeal in all positions. Designed for use with AC power sources, this all-position,cellulose-based electrode provides stable arc characteristics and good penetration.

**Typical applications:**
• Galvanized steel work
• General fabrication
• Railroad cars
• Shipbuilding
• Structural work

**Typical weld metal properties (Chem Pad):**
Carbon..........................................0.12
Manganese....................................0.71
Silicon..........................................0.29
Nickel...........................................0.04
Chromium......................................0.06
Molybdenum..................................0.01
Vanadium......................................0.01

**Typical mechanical properties (AW):**
Tensile Strength (psi) ........82,000 (563 MPa)
Yield Strength (psi)............69,000 (476 MPa)
Elongation % in 2".............26%

**Typical Charpy V-notch impact values (AW):**
Avg. at -20°F (-29°C) 38 ft.lb. (52J)

**Available diameter and recommended operating ranges:**
3/32" (2.4 mm)....................60-90 amps
1/8" (3.2 mm).....................80-125 amps
5/32" (4.0 mm)....................30-160 amps
3/16" (4.8 mm)....................60-190 amps

**Type of current:** AC, DCEP

**Approvals and conformances:**
• AWS A5.1, E6011
• ASME SFA 5.1
• Lloyd's 2m, 2Ym
• CWB-E4311
• ABS E6011

## Hobart® 447A
AWS E6013

When poor fit-up conditions exist, you'll prefer the fast-freeze characteristics of Hobart 447A. Whether put to use with AC or DC power sources, the 447A has a very stable arc and good bead appearance.

**Typical applications:**
• General-purpose fabrication
• Machine parts
• Metal buildings and structures
• Shaft buildup

**Typical weld metal properties (Chem Pad):**
Carbon.........................................0.08
Manganese..................................0.39
Silicon........................................0.25
Nickel.........................................0.04
Chromium....................................0.04
Molybdenum................................0.01
Vanadium ...................................0.01

**Typical mechanical properties (AW):**
Tensile Strength (psi) ........74,000 (514 MPa)
Yield Strength (psi) ............67,000 (463 MPa)
Elongation % in 2" ............30%

**Typical Charpy V-notch impact values:**
Not required

**Available diameter and recommended operating ranges:**
3/32" (2.4 mm)...............40-80 amps
1/8" (3.2 mm)..............70-120 amps
5/32" (4.0 mm)............130-160 amps
3/16" (4.8 mm)............140-220 amps

**Type of current:** AC, DCEN or DCEP

**Approvals and conformances:**
• AWS A5.1, E6013
• ASME SFA 5.1
• ABS E6013

## Hobart® Deckmaster™ 1139
AWS E6022

When you want to get a handle on roof decking, you can rely on Hobart Deckmaster™ 1139. It is a very fluid electrode designed for welding roof decking to support beams with burn-through spot welds. You can also rely on the 1139 for rapid downhill welding when joining light-gauge materials.

**Typical applications:**
• Rapid downhill welding
• Roof decking
• Sheet metal

**Typical weld metal properties (Chem Pad):**
Carbon.........................................0.15
Manganese..................................0.47
Silicon........................................0.15
Phosphorus ................................0.013
Sulphur ......................................0.013

**Typical mechanical properties:**
Transverse tensile strength exceeds 63,000 psi (435 MPa)

**Typical Charpy V-notch impact values:**
Not required

**Available diameter and recommended operating ranges:**
1/8" (3.2 mm)...................110-150 amps
5/32" (4.0 mm).................150-180 amps

**Type of current:** DCEN, DCEP or AC

**Approvals and conformances:**
• AWS A5.1, E6022

*For more information: http://www.hobartbrothers.com*

## Hobart® 14A
AWS E7014

When you are tackling jobs where higher deposition and speed of travel is needed, the Hobart 14A is the electrode to choose. An all-position electrode, Hobart 14A is equipped with a rutile base and iron powder addition to increase deposition rates and give operator appeal. This electrode offers outstanding slag removal and bead appearance and can be operated with AC, DCEP or DCEN power.

**Typical applications:**
• Frames
• Heavy sheet metal
• Machine bases

**Typical weld metal properties (Chem Pad):**
Carbon............................................0.063
Manganese....................................0.42
Silicon ...........................................0.22
Phosphorus ...................................0.013
Sulphur .........................................0.014
Nickel.............................................0.07
Chromium ......................................0.07
Molybdenum ..................................< 0.01
Vanadium .......................................0.02

**Typical mechanical properties (AW):**
Tensile Strength (psi) ........81,000 (561 MPa)
Yield Strength (psi)...........73,000 (505 MPa)
Elongation % in 2" .............24%

**Typical Charpy V-notch impact values:**
Not required

**Available diameter and recommended operating ranges:**
3/32" (2.4 mm)....................70-90 amps
1/8" (3.2 mm)....................120-145 amps
5/32" (4.0 mm)....................140-210 amps
3/16" (4.8 mm)..................180-280 amps

**Type of current:** AC, DCEP or DCEN

**Approvals and conformances:**
• AWS A5.1, E7014
• ASME SFA 5.1, E7014
• CWB E4914
• ABS E7014

## Hobart® 24
AWS E7024, E7024-1

If you want speed, the Hobart 24 high-speed electrode has it. Hobart 24 is exceptionally fast when used down hand in properly designed weld joints or in horizontal fillet welds where equal leg fillets are desired. It has excellent operation on either AC or DCEN power with a drag welding technique. It also meets AWS E7024-1 impact requirements.

**Typical applications:**
• Earthmoving equipment
• Mining machinery
• Plate fabrication
• Railroad cars
• Structurals
• Shipbuilding
• Mobile trailers

**Typical weld metal properties (Chem Pad):**
Carbon............................................0.06
Manganese....................................0.77
Silicon ...........................................0.37
Phosphorus ...................................0.008
Sulphur .........................................0.019
Nickel.............................................0.07
Chromium ......................................0.05
Molybdenum ..................................0.01
Vanadium .......................................0.03

**Typical mechanical properties (AW):**
Tensile Strength (psi) ........82,000 (563 MPa)
Yield Strength (psi)...........72,000 (497 MPa)
Elongation % in 2" .............26%

**Typical Charpy V-notch impact values** (AW) for E7024-1:
Avg. at 0°F (-18°C) 42 ft.lb. (57J)

**Available diameter and recommended operating ranges:**
1/8 " (3.2 mm)....................130-150 amps
5/32" (4.0 mm)..................180-225 amps
3/16" (4.8 mm)..................200-280 amps
7/32" (5.6 mm)..................250-320 amps
1/4" (6.4 mm)....................300-360 amps

**Type of current:** AC, DCEN or DCEP

**Approvals and conformances:**
• AWS A5.1, E7024, E7024-1
• ASME SFA 5.1, E7024
• ABS 3
• CWB E4924-1

*For more information: http://www.hobartbrothers.com*

## Hobart® 418
AWS E7018 H4R, E7018-1 H4R

Hobart 418 gives you all the flexibility you need in a general-purpose, low-hydrogen, mild steel electrode. It also has good out-of-position welding capabilities and provides an X-ray quality deposit. And this unique electrode is ideal for tacking prior to finish welding with Fabshield self-shielded, tubular wire. That's because the construction of the Hobart 418 allows removal of all the slag from the self-shielded wire.

### Typical applications:
• Field erections, steel structures
• Jobs where low-hydrogen weld metal in the tensile strength range of 70,000 psi is required
• Low alloy structurals
• Low-, medium- and high-carbon steels
• Offshore rigs, power plants

### Typical weld metal properties (Chem Pad):
| | |
|---|---|
| Carbon | 0.04 |
| Manganese | 0.95 |
| Silicon | 0.54 |
| Phosphorus | 0.012 |
| Sulphur | 0.014 |
| Nickel | 0.07 |
| Chromium | 0.07 |
| Molybdenum | 0.03 |
| Vanadium | < 0.01 |

### Typical mechanical properties (AW):
Tensile Strength (psi) ....... 78,000 (541 MPa)
Yield Strength (psi) ............ 64,000 (441 MPa)
Elongation % in 2" .............. 29%

### Typical Charpy V-notch impact values (AW):
Avg. at -50°F (-46°C) 86 ft.lb. (116J)

### Available diameter and recommended operating ranges:
| | |
|---|---|
| 3/32" (2.4 mm) | 80-100 amps |
| 1/8" (3.2 mm) | 90-150 amps |
| 5/32" (4.0 mm) | 110-230 amps |
| 3/16" (4.8 mm) | 150-300 amps |
| 7/32" (5.6 mm) | 220-350 amps |
| 1/4" (6.4 mm) | 270-380 amps |

**Type of current:** DCEP or AC

### Approvals and conformances:
• AWS A5.1, E7018 H4R, E7018-1 H4R
• ASME SFA 5.1, E7018
• ABS 3H5, 3Y
• Lloyd's BF3.3YH5
• CWB E4918-1 H4

## Hobart® 718MC
AWS E7018 H4R, E7018(M)-1 H4R

You can take control with the electrode that's formulated and manufactured to give you excellent moisture resistance, good out-of-position welding capabilities and an X-ray quality deposit. The 718MC meets the requirements of military spec. Mil-E-22200/10, including moisture absorption limits of .10% max. as opened and .20% max. after 9 hrs. at 80°F and 80% relative humidity.

### Typical applications:
• Barge offshore rigs, shipbuilding
• Boiler code applications
• Field erection, steel structures
• Petrochemical plants, power plants
• Railcar and locomotive construction
• Welding of enameling steels; free machining steels; low alloy structurals; and low, medium or high carbon steels
• Weldments in low-temperature environments where low-temperature impacts are important

### Typical weld metal properties (Chem Pad):
| | |
|---|---|
| Carbon | 0.04 |
| Manganese | 0.92 |
| Silicon | 0.25 |
| Phosphorus | 0.011 |
| Sulphur | 0.016 |
| Nickel | 0.07 |
| Chromium | 0.06 |
| Molybdenum | < 0.01 |
| Vanadium | < 0.01 |

### Typical mechanical properties (AW):
Tensile Strength (psi) ........ 80,000 (550 MPa)
Yield Strength (psi) ............ 69,000 (478 MPa)
Elongation % in 2" ............. 28%

### Typical Charpy V-notch impact values (AW):
Avg. at -50°F (-46°C) 106 ft.lb. (144J)

### Available diameter and recommended operating ranges:
| | |
|---|---|
| 3/32" (2.4 mm) | 70-110 amps |
| 1/8" (3.2 mm) | 90-165 amps |
| 5/32" (4.0 mm) | 125-220 amps |
| 3/16" (4.8 mm) | 160-300 amps |
| 7/32" (5.6 mm) | 260-340 amps |
| 1/4" (6.4 mm) | 270-380 amps |

**Type of current:** DCEP or AC

### Approvals and conformances:
• AWS A5.1, E7018 H4R, E7018 -1H4R
• ABS 3H5, 3Y
• ASME SFA 5.1, E7018
• MIL-E-22200/10

## Hobart® 18AC
AWS E7018 H8

Highly recommended for applications using small 208/230V, single phase AC welders, 18AC has good operator appeal, excellent re-striking characteristics and an extremely stable arc. 18AC is also an excellent choice for skip or tack welds. The slag is self-removing in most applications. 18AC will work well on all AC power sources and performs exceptionally well on utility-type welders.

**Typical applications:**
• Low-, medium- and high-carbon steels
• Skip or tack welds
• Shops, farms, hobbyist
• Some high-strength low alloy steels

**Typical weld metal properties (Chem Pad):**
Carbon..........................................0.04
Manganese....................................0.67
Silicon...........................................0.29
Chromium......................................0.07
Molybdenum..................................0.01
Nickel............................................0.08
Vanadium......................................0.02
Phosphorus ..................................0.008
Sulphur .........................................0.01

**Typical mechanical properties (AW):**
Tensile Strength (psi) ........88,000 (607 MPa)
Yield Strength (psi)............77,000 (532 MPa)
Elongation % in 2" .............30%

**Typical Charpy V-notch impact values (AW):**
Avg. at -20°F (-29°C) 30 ft.lb. (41J)

**Available diameter and recommended operating ranges:**
3/32" (2.4 mm)...................70-110 amps
1/8" (3.2 mm).....................90-165 amps
5/32" (4.0 mm).................125-220 amps

**Type of current:** AC, DCEN or DCEP

**Approvals and conformances:**
• AWS A5.1, E7018 H8
• ASME SFA 5.1, E7018

*For more information: http://www.hobartbrothers.com*

# Low Alloy Steel Electrodes

## Hoballoy® 7018A1
AWS E7018-A1 H4R

For pressure vessel applications, the Hoballoy 7018A1 is an outstanding choice. When welding .50% molybdenum steel and other low alloy steels, the Hoballoy 7018A1 offers resistance to moisture reabsorption. This important feature helps prevent hydrogen cracking and aids in the elimination of starting porosity.

**Typical applications:**
• Construction and maintenance of boilers
• Piping
• Tubing

**Typical weld metal properties (Chem Pad):**

| | |
|---|---|
| Carbon | 0.03 |
| Manganese | 0.77 |
| Silicon | 0.42 |
| Phosphorus | 0.02 |
| Sulphur | 0.01 |
| Molybdenum | 0.52 |

**Typical mechanical properties
(stress relieve 1 hour @ 1150°F):**
Tensile Strength (psi) ........85,000 (587 MPa)
Yield Strength (psi) ............74,000 (507 MPa)
Elongation % in 2" .............28%

**Typical Charpy V-notch impact values**
Not required

**Available diameter and
recommended operating ranges:**
3/32" (2.4 mm) .................... 70-110 amps
1/8" (3.2 mm) ..................... 90-160 amps
5/32" (4.0 mm) .................. 130-220 amps

**Type of current:** DCEP or AC

**Approvals and conformances:**
• AWS A5.5, E7018-A1 H4R
• ASME SFA 5.5, E7018-A1
• ABS E7018-A1

## Hoballoy® 8018B2
AWS E8018-B2 H4R

Hoballoy 8018B2 is an outstanding electrode for welding higher strength steels requiring tensile strengths of 80,000 lbs. or more. Ideal for welding in conditions of high heat or humidity, it features a specially formulated coating that's designed to reduce moisture pick-up and thus help keep hydrogen cracking and starting porosity to a minimum.

**Typical applications:**
• Fabrication and maintenance of boilers and associated piping
• Steels such as 1-1/4 Cr–1/2 Mo and 1/2 Cr–1/2 Mo

**Typical weld metal properties (Chem Pad):**

| | |
|---|---|
| Carbon | 0.07 |
| Manganese | 0.73 |
| Silicon | 0.61 |
| Phosphorus | 0.01 |
| Sulphur | 0.01 |
| Chromium | 1.33 |
| Molybdenum | 0.55 |

**Typical mechanical properties
(stress relieve 1 hour @ 1275°F):**
Tensile Strength (psi) ........103,000 (710 MPa)
Yield Strength (psi) ............90,000 (621 MPa)
Elongation % in 2" .............22%

**Typical Charpy V-notch impact values**
Not required

**Available diameter and
recommended operating ranges:**
3/32" (2.4 mm) .................... 70-110 amps
1/8" (3.2 mm) ..................... 90-160 amps
5/32" (4.0 mm) .................. 130-220 amps
3/16" (4.8 mm) .................. 200-300 amps

**Type of current:** DCEP or AC

**Approvals and conformances:**
• AWS A5.5, E8018-B2 H4R
• ASME SFA 5.5, E8018-B2
• ABS E8018-B2

*For more information: http://www.hobartbrothers.com*

## Hoballoy® 8018C1
AWS E8018-C1 H4

Hoballoy 8018C1 is a high-quality electrode that's designed for applications of 2% nickel deposits and the welding of nickel-bearing steels for low temperature applications where toughness of the weld metal is important. It provides good puddle control, excellent wetting action and tie-in and offers good arc characteristics as well as excellent notch toughness (65 ft. lbs. at -75°F) and easy slag removal. Hoballoy 8018C1 is also great for welding in conditions of high heat or humidity as it features a specially-formulated coating that's designed to minimize hydrogen cracking and starting porosity.

### Typical applications:
• Shipbuilding
• Piping
• Tanks used in the storage of gases

### Typical weld metal properties (Chem Pad):
| | |
|---|---|
| Carbon | 0.04 |
| Manganese | 1.01 |
| Silicon | 0.26 |
| Phosphorus | 0.01 |
| Sulphur | 0.01 |
| Nickel | 2.57 |

### Typical mechanical properties
(stress relieve 1 hour @ 1125°F):
Tensile Strength (psi) ........93,000 (643 MPa)
Yield Strength (psi) ...........79,000 (543 MPa)
Elongation % in 2" ............26%

### Typical Charpy V-notch impact values (SR):
Avg. at -75°F (-59°C) 59 ft.lb. (80J)

### Available diameter and
recommended operating ranges:
3/32" (2.4 mm) .................... 70-110 amps
1/8" (3.2 mm) ...................... 90-160 amps
5/32" (4.0 mm) ................. 130-220 amps
3/16" (4 8 mm) ................. 200-300 amps

**Type of current:** DCEP or AC

### Approvals and conformances:
• AWS A5.5, E8018-C1 H4
• ASME SFA 5.5, E8018-C1 H4
• ABS E8018-C1

## Hoballoy® 8018C3
AWS E8018-C3 H4

Hoballoy 8018-C3 electrodes are designed for high tensile steels requiring 1% nickel weld deposits.

### Typical applications:
• Commercial using 80,000 tensile steels
• Military using 80,000 tensile steels
• Welding of AR and T-1 steels

### Typical weld metal properties (Chem Pad):
| | |
|---|---|
| Carbon | 0.04 |
| Manganese | 0.98 |
| Silicon | 0.26 |
| Phosphorus | 0.01 |
| Sulphur | 0.01 |
| Nickel | 0.89 |
| Chromium | 0.07 |
| Molybdenum | 0.09 |
| Vanadium | 0.01 |

### Typical mechanical properties (AW):
Tensile Strength (psi) ........84,000 (576 MPa)
Yield Strength (psi) ...........73,000 (503 MPa)
Elongation % in 2" ............30%

### Typical Charpy V-notch impact values (AW):
Avg. at -40°F (-40°C) 98 ft.lb. (133J)

### Available diameter and
recommended operating ranges:
3/32" (2.4 mm) .................... 70-110 amps
1/8" (3.2 mm) ...................... 90-160 amps
5/32" (4.0 mm) ................. 130-220 amps
3/16" (4.8 mm) ................. 200-300 amps

**Type of current:** DCEP or AC

### Approvals and conformances:
• AWS A5.5, E8018-C3 H4
• ASME SFA 5.5, E8018-C3 H4
• MIL-E-22200/1 (1/8, 5/32)
• ABS E8018-C3

*For more information: http://www.hobartbrothers.com*

# Low Alloy Steel Electrodes

## Hoballoy® 9018B3

AWS E9018-B3 H4R

Hobart's Hoballoy 9018B3 is an outstanding electrode that's designed for welding higher strength steel applications. It offers better corrosion resistance than carbon electrodes and features a special coating that's formulated to reduce moisture pick-up, helping to minimize hydrogen cracking and starting porosity.

**Typical applications:**
- Chrome-moly pipes
- Castings
- Forgings
- Boiler work

**Typical weld metal properties (Chem Pad):**

| | |
|---|---|
| Carbon | 0.08 |
| Manganese | 0.68 |
| Silicon | 0.55 |
| Phosphorus | 0.02 |
| Sulphur | 0.01 |
| Chromium | 2.39 |
| Molybdenum | 1.05 |

**Typical mechanical properties (stress relieve 1 hour @ 1275°F):**

Tensile Strength (psi) ........ 109,000 (750 MPa)
Yield Strength (psi) ............ 93,000 (640 MPa)
Elongation % in 2" ............ 21%

**Typical Charpy V-notch impact values**
Not required

**Available diameter and recommended operating ranges:**

3/32" (2.4 mm) ................... 70-110 amps
1/8" (3.2 mm) ..................... 90-160 amps
5/32" (4.0 mm) ................. 130-220 amps
3/16" (4.8 mm) ................. 200-300 amps

**Type of current:** DCEP or AC

**Approvals and conformances:**
- AWS A5.5, E9018-B3 H4R
- ASME SFA 5.5, E9018-B3 H4R
- ABS E9018-B3

## Hoballoy® 9018M

AWS E9018-M H4R

Hoballoy 9018M is an outstanding electrode that's designed for applications requiring tensile strengths of at least 90,000 psi. An ideal choice for conditions of high heat and humidity, Hoballoy 9018M has a specially formulated coating that reduces moisture pick-up, which helps to minimize hydrogen cracking and starting porosity.

**Typical applications:**
- Joining HY-90 steel
- Joining HY-80 steel
- Joining T-1 steel
- Joining other high-tensile steels

**Typical weld metal properties (Chem Pad):**

| | |
|---|---|
| Carbon | 0.06 |
| Manganese | 0.92 |
| Silicon | 0.16 |
| Phosphorus | 0.014 |
| Sulphur | 0.016 |
| Nickel | 1.63 |
| Chromium | 0.08 |
| Molybdenum | 0.26 |
| Vanadium | 0.01 |

**Typical mechanical properties (AW):**

Tensile Strength (psi) ........ 97,000 (672 MPa)
Yield Strength (psi) ............ 84,000 (583 MPa)
Elongation % in 2" ............ 26%

**Typical Charpy V-notch impact values (AW):**
Avg. at -60°F (-51°C) 60 ft.lb. (81J)

**Available diameter and recommended operating ranges:**

3/32" (2.4 mm) ................... 70-110 amps
1/8" (3.2 mm) ..................... 90-160 amps
5/32" (4.0 mm) ................. 130-220 amps
3/16" (4.8 mm) ................. 200-300 amps

**Type of current:** DCEP or AC

**Approvals and conformances:**
- AWS A5.5, E9018-M H4R
- ASME SFA 5.5, E9018-M H4R
- ABS E9018-M
- DNV 5 YH5

## Hoballoy® 10018D2
AWS E10018-D2 H4R

A high-quality electrode, Hoballoy 10018D2 is designed for the welding of high tensile steels and manganese-molybdenum steels requiring tensile strengths of at least 100,000 psi. It has high operator appeal and offers a wide variety of welding advantages including good arc characteristics, ductility, crackresistance, easy slag removal, and low spatter and smoke. Plus, Hoballoy 10018D2 is an ideal choice for conditions of high heat and humidity because it features a special coating that's designed to reduce moisture pick-up, which also helps to minimize hydrogen cracking and starting porosity.

**Typical applications:**
• Manganese-moly castings
• Alloy forgings
• Structurals
• Pressure vessel applications in either the as welded or stress-relieved condition

**Typical weld metal properties (Chem Pad):**
Carbon ............................................0.05
Manganese ......................................1.96
Silicon .............................................0.17
Phosphorus .....................................0.02
Sulphur ............................................0.01
Molybdenum ....................................0.40
Nickel ..............................................0.47

**Typical mechanical properties (stress relieve 1 hour @ 1150°F):**
Tensile Strength (psi) ........109,000 (750 MPa)
Yield Strength (psi) ............96,000 (661 MPa)
Elongation % in 2" .............23%

**Typical Charpy V-notch impact values (SR):**
Avg. at -60°F (-51°C) 40 ft.lb. (54J)

**Available diameter and recommended operating ranges:**
3/32" (2.4 mm) .....................70-110 amps
1/8" (3.2 mm) .......................90-160 amps
5/32" (4.0 mm) .................130-220 amps
3/16" (4.8 mm) .................200-300 amps

**Type of current:** DCEP or AC

**Approvals and conformances:**
• AWS A5.5, E10018-D2 H4R
• ASME SFA 5.5, E10018-D2 H4R

## Hoballoy® 11018M
AWS E11018-M H4R

Designed for military applications and other projects that require weld joints with tensile strengths of at least 110,000 psi, Hoballoy 11018M offers a wide range of welding advantages that will improve your welding productivity – good arc characteristics, excellent puddle control with good wetting action and tie-in, and easy slag removal. Ideal for conditions of high heat and humidity, it features a special coating that's designed to reduce moisture pick-up, helping to minimize hydrogen cracking and starting porosity. Hoballoy 11018M also offers good ductility, good crack resistance and high notch toughness even at temperatures as low as -60°F.

**Typical applications:**
• Low-alloy steels including HY-80, HY-90 and T-1

**Typical weld metal properties (Chem Pad):**
Carbon ............................................0.04
Manganese ......................................1.57
Silicon .............................................0.34
Nickel ..............................................1.99
Phosphorus .....................................0.015
Sulphur ............................................0.010
Molybdenum ....................................0.29
Chromium ........................................0.19
Vanadium ........................................0.010

**Typical mechanical properties (AW):**
Tensile Strength (psi) ........116,000 (799 MPa)
Yield Strength (psi) ............107,000 (736 MPa)
Elongation % in 2" .............22%

**Typical Charpy V-notch impact values (AW):**
Avg. at -60°F (-51°C) 56 ft.lb. (76J)

**Available diameter and recommended operating ranges:**
3/32" (2.4 mm) .....................75-115 amps
1/8" (3.2 mm) .......................90-160 amps
5/32" (4.0 mm) .................130-220 amps
3/16" (4.8 mm) .................200-300 amps
1/4" (6.4 mm) ...................300-400 amps

**Type of current:** DCEP

**Approvals and conformances:**
• AWS A5.5, E11018-M H4R
• ASME SFA 5.5, E11018-M
• ABS E11018M
• MIL-E-222001, (1/8)
• DNV 5Y69

*For more information: http://www.hobartbrothers.com*

## Hoballoy® 12018M
AWS E12018-M H4R

Hoballoy 12018M is designed for welding high tensile steels requiring weld joints with tensile strengths of at least 120,000 psi. It offers a wide variety of welding advantages that include: good arc characteristics, ductility, crack-resistance, easy slag removal, and low spatter and smoke. Hoballoy 12018M also works extremely well under conditions of high heat and humidity because its special coating is designed to reduce moisture pick-up, which also helps to keep hydrogen cracking and starting porosity to a minimum.

### Typical applications:
• Low-alloy steels
• Forgings
• Castings
• Plate and pressure vessels

### Typical weld metal properties (Chem Pad):
Carbon...........................................0.05
Manganese...................................1.55
Silicon...........................................0.42
Phosphorus ..................................0.020
Sulphur .........................................0.013
Nickel.............................................1.76
Molybdenum...................................0.39
Chromium.......................................0.63
Vanadium ......................................0.01

### Typical mechanical properties (AW):
Tensile Strength (psi) ........130,000 (895 MPa)
Yield Strength (psi)............118,000 (814 MPa)
Elongation % in 2" ............19%

### Typical Charpy V-notch impact values (AW):
Avg. at -60°F (-51°C) 24 ft.lb. (32J)

### Available diameter and recommended operating ranges:
3/32" (2.4 mm)....................70-110 amps
1/8" (3.2 mm)......................90-160 amps
5/32" (4.0 mm)....................130-220 amps
3/16" (4.8 mm).................200-300 amps

### Type of current: DCEP

### Approvals and conformances:
• AWS A5.5, E12018-M H4R
• ASME SFA 5.5, E12018-M H4R
• ABS E12018M

# Stainless Steel Electrodes

## 308/308L Sterling®AP
AWS E308-16, E308L-16

Primarily designed for welding type 308L base metal with low or medium carbon content, the 308/308L Sterling AP contains low carbon to avert carbide precipitation during welding as well as weld service. Excellent for welding 18 Cr-8 Ni steels. It has a smooth running arc that results in a uniform weld bead that is flat to slightly convex. Note: Actual certs are included in every master carton of stainless stick electrodes at no charge.

**Typical applications:**
• Food and beverage
• Petrochemical plants
• Pulp and paper
• Other general fabrication on stainless steel

**Typical weld metal properties (Chem Pad):**

|  |  | AWS Spec E308-16 |
| --- | --- | --- |
| Carbon | 0.03 | .08 max |
| Manganese | 1.00 | .5-2.25 |
| Phosphorus | 0.018 | .04 max |
| Sulphur | 0.010 | .03 max |
| Silicon | 0.50 | .90 max |
| Copper | 0.10 | .75 max |
| Chromium | 19.00 | 18.0-21.0 |
| Nickel | 10.00 | 9.0-11.0 |
| Molybdenum | 0.10 | .75 max |

**Typical mechanical properties (AW):**

|  |  | AWS Spec E308-16 |
| --- | --- | --- |
| Tensile Strength (psi) | 83,000 | 80,000 |
| Yield Strength (psi) | 64,000 | not req. |
| Elongation % in 2" | 42% | 35% |
| DeLong Ferrite Range | 4-10 | not req. |

**Available diameter and recommended operating ranges:**

3/32" (2.4 mm) ..................45-80 amps
1/8" (3.2 mm) ....................55-120 amps
5/32 " (4.0 mm) .................65-170 amps
3/16" (4.8 mm) ................160-205 amps
1/4" (6.4 mm) ..................180-225 amps

**Type of current:** DCEP or AC

## 309/309L Sterling® AP
AWS E309-16-16, E309L-16

309/309L Sterling AP is a lower carbon version of the 309(H) Sterling AP. Low carbon content makes it excellent for applications where reduced susceptibility to sensitization during high temperature service is necessary. Outstanding for dissimilar metal welding such as weld overlay or for welding type 309 stainless steel to mild or low alloy steels. It has a smooth running arc that results in a uniform weld bead that is flat to slightly convex. Note: Actual certs are included in every master carton of stainless stick electrodes at no charge.

**Typical applications:**
• Food and beverage
• Petrochemical plants
• Pulp and paper
• Other general fabrication on stainless steel

**Typical weld metal properties (Chem Pad):**

|  |  | AWS Spec E309-16 |
| --- | --- | --- |
| Carbon | 0.03 | .15 max |
| Manganese | 1.05 | .5-2.25 |
| Phosphorus | 0.020 | .04 max |
| Sulphur | 0.016 | .03 max |
| Silicon | 0.45 | .90 max |
| Copper | 0.10 | .75 max |
| Chromium | 23.00 | 22.0-25.0 |
| Nickel | 13.50 | 12.0-14.0 |
| Molybdenum | 0.10 | .75 max |

**Typical mechanical properties (AW):**

|  |  | AWS Spec E309-16 |
| --- | --- | --- |
| Tensile Strength (psi) | 79,000 | 80,000 |
| Yield Strength (psi) | 64,000 | not req. |
| Elongation % in 2" | 38% | 35% |
| DeLong Ferrite Range | 4-15 | not req. |

**Available diameter and recommended operating ranges:**

3/32" (2.4 mm) ..................45-80 amps
1/8" (3.2 mm) ....................55-120 amps
5/32" (4.0 mm) .................65-170 amps
3/16" (4.8 mm) ................160-205 amps
1/4" (6.4 mm) ..................180-225 amps

**Type of current:** DCEP or AC

*Note: Sterling is a registered trademark of Hobart Brothers Company.*

## 310 Sterling® AP
AWS E310-16

The all position 310 Sterling AP is ideal for welding base metal of similar composition, when the stainless base metal is of unknown composition, as well as for dissimilar metals. Also excellent for welding and building up parts for heat treatment and case hardening furnaces, cement kilns and other burners subject to high temperature oxidation in a non-sulphurous atmosphere It has a smooth running arc that results in a uniform bead that is flat to slightly convex. Note: Actual certs are included in every master carton of stainless stick electrodes at no charge.

**Typical applications:**
• Fabrication of preheater tubes for pressure vessels and other high temperature applications.

**Typical weld metal properties (Chem Pad):**

|  |  | AWS Spec. |
|---|---|---|
| Carbon | 0.14 | .08-.20 max |
| Manganese | 2.02 | 1.0-2.5 |
| Phosphorus | 0.015 | .03 max |
| Sulphur | 0.015 | .03 max |
| Silicon | 0.46 | .75 max |
| Copper | 0.15 | .75 max |
| Chromium | 26.12 | 25.0-28.0 |
| Nickel | 21.00 | 20.0-22.5 |
| Molybdenum | 0.12 | .75 max |

**Typical mechanical properties (AW):**

|  |  | AWS Spec. |
|---|---|---|
| Tensile Strength (psi) | 86,000 | 80,000 |
| Yield Strength (psi) | 63,000 | not req. |
| Elongation % in 2" | 40% | 35% |
| DeLong Ferrite Range | 0 | not req. |

**Available diameter and recommended operating ranges:**
3/32" (2.4 mm) ....................45-80 amps
1/8" (3.2 mm) ......................55-120 amps
5/32" (4.0 mm) ...................65-170 amps
3/16" (4.8 mm) .................160-205 amps

**Type of current:** DCEP or AC

## 312 Sterling® AP
AWS E312-16

Ideal for new fabrication or repair maintenance applications, 312 Sterling AP is designed for welding dissimilar joints of Type 312 metals. 312 Sterling AP can be used on hardenable steels, steel armor and generally hard to weld steels, offering outstanding performance with a directional arc and self-detaching slag. With capabilities considered equal to "special maintenance" electrodes, 312 Sterling AP is available at much less than the "special maintenance" price. It has a smooth running arc that results in a uniform bead that is flat to slightly convex.

**Typical applications:**
• Joining dissimilar steels or hard-to-weld steels
• Single and multiple pass DCEP, AC.

**Typical weld metal properties (Chem Pad):**

|  |  | AWS Spec. |
|---|---|---|
| Carbon | 0.07 | .15 max |
| Manganese | 0.80 | .05-2.5 |
| Phosphorus | 0.015 | .04 max |
| Sulphur | 0.017 | .03 max |
| Silicon | 0.40 | .90 max |
| Copper | 0.15 | .75 max |
| Chromium | 28.50 | 28.0-32.0 |
| Nickel | 9.10 | 8.0-10.5 |
| Molybdenum | 0.11 | .75 max |

**Typical mechanical properties (AW):**

|  |  | AWS Spec. |
|---|---|---|
| Tensile Strength (psi) | 115,000 | 95,000 |
| Yield Strength (psi) | 95,000 | not req. |
| Elongation % in 2 | 25% | 22% |
| DeLong Ferrite Range | 25-80 | not req. |

**Available diameter and recommended operating ranges:**
3/32" (2.4 mm) ....................45-80 amps
1/8" (3.2 mm) ......................55-120 amps
5/32" (4.0 mm) ...................65-170 amps
3/16" (4.8 mm) .................160-205 amps

**Type of current:** DCEP or AC

*Note: Sterling is a registered trademark of Hobart Brothers Company.*

## 316/316L Sterling® AP
AWS E316-16, E316H-16

316/316L Sterling AP possesses properties similar to 316/316H Sterling AP except with a much lower carbon content which reduces susceptibility to sensitization during welding. The welds show high resistance to corrosion and fissuring. This makes it an outstanding choice for critical applications. Excellent for welding stainless steel types 316, 316-L and Note: Actual certs are included in every master carton of stainless stick electrodes at no charge.

**Typical applications:**
• Food and beverage
• Petrochemical plants,
• Pulp and paper
• Other general fabrication on stainless steel

The information contained or otherwise referenced herein is presented only as "typical without guarantee or warranty, and Hobart expressly disclaims any liability incurred from any reliance thereon. Typical data are obtained when welded and tested in accordance with AWS specification. Other tests and precedures may produce different results. No data is to be construed as a recommendation for any welding condition or technique not contolled by Hobart.

**Typical weld metal properties (Chem Pad):**

|  |  | AWS Spec E316-16 |
|---|---|---|
| Carbon | 0.02 | .08 max |
| Manganese | 1.05 | .5-2.25 |
| Phosphorus | 0.015 | .04 max |
| Sulphur | 0.015 | .03 max |
| Silicon | 0.48 | .90 max |
| Copper | 0.20 | .75 max |
| Chromium | 18.20 | 17.0-20.0 |
| Nickel | 13.00 | 11.0-14.0 |
| Molybdenum | 2.30 | 2.0-3.0 |

**Typical mechanical properties (AW):**

|  |  | AWS Spec E316-16 |
|---|---|---|
| Tensile Strength (psi) | 82,000 | 75,000 |
| Yield Strength (psi) | 61,000 | not req. |
| Elongation % in 2" | 42% | 30% |
| DeLong Ferrite Range | 2-6 | not req. |

**Available diameter and recommended operating ranges:**
3/32" (2.4 mm) ................... 45-80 amps
1/8" (3.2 mm) ..................... 55-120 amps
5/32" (4.0 mm) ................... 65-170 amps
3/16" (4.8 mm) ................. 160-205 amps

**Type of current:** DCEP or AC

*For more information: http://www.hobartbrothers.com*

## Hardalloy® 148

Hardalloy® 148 deposit is a high carbonchromium austenitic plus carbide alloy steel suited to overlay surfaces subjected to light abrasion accompanied by impact. It has excellent metal-to-metal frictional wear resistance, and the deposit retains hardness at temperatures up to 1200°F.

### Typical Applications:
• Gyratory crusher mantles & cones
• Ingot tongs
• Mill guides
• Pulleys
• Slurry mixer paddles

### Typical Deposit Analysis %:
Carbon..........................................1.80
Manganese...................................0.60
Silicon...........................................1.80
Chromium....................................30.00
Nickel............................................3.00
Molybdenum................................1.50
Iron ..............................................Bal.

### Typical Properties:
Low stress abrasion – excellent.
Machinability – Grinding only.
Typical Hardness, Rc

| No. of Layers | 1020 Steel | 12-14% Mn Steel |
|---|---|---|
| 1 | 36RC | 35RC |
| 2 | 39RC | 38RC |
| 3 | 43RC | 40RC |

Cannot be flame cut.
Little or no relief-check cracks.
Maintains hot hardness to 1200°F.

### Optimum Current:

| Diameter | Amps |
|---|---|
| 1/8" | 120 |
| 5/32" | 160 |
| 3/16" | 175 |

**Polarity:** DCEP Preferred or AC

## Hardalloy® 118

Hardalloy® 118 deposit is a work hardening austenitic manganese steel alloy. It is designed for the build-up and joining of austenitic manganese steels only. Provides a good wear resistance under heavy impact conditions. Weld deposits are extremely tough, and work hardens rapidly.

**Typical Applications:**
• Crusher jaws & cones
• Crusher rolls
• Dredge pump casings, impellers, & side plates
• Gyratory crusher mantles & cones
• Hammer mill hammers
• Impactor crusher bars
• Manganese bucket teeth
• Manganese steel railroad crossovers & frogs
• Sizing screens

**Typical Deposit Analysis %:**
Carbon..........................................0.80
Manganese.................................16.50
Silicon..........................................0.50
Chromium....................................5.00
Nickel...........................................0.30
Iron .............................................Bal.

**Typical Properties:**
Tensile Strength ...............127,000 psi
Yield Strength.....................78,000 psi
Elongation in 2"...........................50%
Machinability – Difficult
Hardness:
  As Deposited ......................18-22 Rc
  Work Hardened .................50-55 Rc
Flame cutting is difficult.
Nonmagnetic.

**Optimum Current:**

| Diameter | Amps |
| --- | --- |
| 1/8" | 120 |
| 5/32" | 180 |
| 3/16" | 230 |
| 1/4" | 280 |

**Polarity:** DCEP Preferred or AC

## Hardalloy® 32

Hardalloy® 32 deposit is a heat treatable alloy steel suited for the build-up of carbon and low alloy steels only. The weld metal is sound, and the good compressive strength makes it an excellent base for hard surfacing. It has excellent resistance to cracking and checking in heavy thicknesses.

**Typical Applications:**
• Bucket teeth & lips
• Coupling boxes
• Crane wheels
• Dragline buckets & chain
• Dredge ladder rolls
• Gear teeth
• Grizzly bars & fingers
• Kiln trunnions
• Mine car wheels
• Steel Shafts
• Tractor idlers & rollers
• Wobbler ends

**Typical Deposit Analysis %:**
Carbon..........................................0.18
Manganese.................................. 0.90
Silicon..........................................0.60
Chromium .....................................0.70
Molybdenum.................................0.30
Iron .............................................Bal.

**Typical Properties:**
Machinability................... Excellent
Typical Hardness, Rc

| No. of Layers | 1020 Steel |
| --- | --- |
| 1-2 | 17-20 |
| 3-8 | 25-30 |

Can be flame cut.
Deposit is strongly magnetic.
Depoosit is heat treatable and forgeable.

**Optimum Current**

| Diameter | Amps |
| --- | --- |
| 1/8" | 140 |
| 5/32" | 180 |
| 3/16" | 220 |
| 1/4" | 300 |

**Polarity:** DCEP Preferred or AC

## Hardalloy® 140

Hardalloy® 140 deposits a high chromium carbide alloy steel. It can be used to overlay surfaces subjected to high abrasion coupled with some impact. It maintains its wear resistance to a temperature of 1200°F and offers some corrosion resistance. Hardalloy 140 is designed for carbon, low alloy or austenitic manganese base metals or a weld metal base of Hardalloy 32, Hardalloy 118, or Chrome-Mang™.

### Typical Applications:
- Ammonia knives
- Augers
- Bucket teeth & lips
- Bulldozer blades
- Cement chutes
- Crusher jaws & cones
- Crusher rolls
- Cultivator chisels & sweeps
- Dredge cutter heads & teeth
- Dredge pump side plates
- Grizzly bars & fingers
- Hammer mill hammers
- Impactor crusher bars
- Manganese pump sheels
- Mill guides
- Muller tires
- Pipeline ball joints
- Plow shares
- Scraper blades
- Screw conveyers
- Sheepsfoot tampers
- Sizing screens

### Typical Deposit Analysis %:
Carbon...........................................3.00
Manganese................................. 0.40
Silicon...........................................2.00
Chromium.................................30.00
Molybdenum...............................0.70
Iron ...........................................Bal.

### Typical Properties:
Machinability . . . . . . . . . . .Grinding only
Typical Hardness, Rc

| No. of Layers | 1020 Steel | 12-14% Mn Steel |
|---|---|---|
| 1 | 53 | 50 |
| 2 | 57 | 55 |
| 3 | 54 | 56 |

Cannot be flame cut.
Deposit will relief-check crack.
Deposit maintains hot hardness to 1200°F.

### Optimum Current:

| Diameter | Amps |
|---|---|
| 1/8" | 120 |
| 5/32" | 155 |
| 3/16" | 190 |

**Polarity:** DCEP Preferred or AC

## QUANTUM ARC™ 3
AWS ER70S-3

When you need a wire versatile enough for general fabrication or a wire that can handle argon-rich mixtures like 75% Ar/25% $CO_2$ with ease, choose Hobart Quantum Arc 3. It's a precision mix of silicon and manganese in a deoxidized wire that makes short-circuiting and spray-transfer applications go smoothly.

**Typical applications:**
• Auto frames
• General fabrication
• Farm equipment
• Ornamental iron fabrication
• Railcars
• Sheet metal
• Storage bins

**Typical wire chemistry (as manufactured):**
Carbon..........................................0.08
Manganese....................................1.19
Silicon..........................................0.46
Phosphorus ..................................0.015
Sulphur .........................................0.010
Copper..........................................0.20

**Typical weld metal properties (Chem Pad):**
100% $CO_2$
Carbon.......................................... 0.09
Manganese.................................. 0.90
Silicon.......................................... 0.35
Phosphorus ................................ 0.11
Sulphur ........................................0.012

**Typical mechanical properties (AW):**
$CO_2$
Tensile Strength (psi) ........77,000 (531 MPa)
Yield Strength (psi)............63,000 (436 MPa)
Elongation % in 2" .............26%

**Typical Charpy V-notch impact values (AW):**
Avg. at 0°F (-18°C), $CO_2$ 83 ft.lb. (113J)

**Approvals and Conformances:**
• AWS A5.18, ER70S-3
• ASME SFA 5.18, ER70S-3
• CWB ER49S-3

## QUANTUM ARC™ 6
AWS ER70S-6

When the task demands excellent weldability for $CO_2$ or Ar/$CO_2$ mixtures and you have rusty, scaly or oily plates, choose the mild steel electrode with deoxidizers powerful enough to handle the job. Hobart Quantum Arc 6 is formulated to ensure sound, porosity-free welds over a wide range of general shop fabrications.

**Typical applications:**
• Construction work
• Farm implement fabrication
• General shop work
• Steel castings or forging salvage
• Shaft buildup
• Tanks
• Auto and truck assemblies

Typical wire chemistry (as manufactured):
Carbon..........................................0.08
Manganese....................................1.45
Silicon..........................................0.81
Phosphorus ..................................0.009
Sulphur .........................................0.015

**Typical mechanical properties (AW):**
$CO_2$
Tensile Strength (psi) ........85,000 (587 MPa)
Yield Strength (psi)............70,000 (485 MPa)
Elongation % in 2" .............26%

**Typical Charpy V-notch impact values (AW):**
Avg. at -20°F (-29°C), $CO_2$ 50 ft.lb. (67J)

**Approvals and Conformances:**
• AWS A5.18, ER70S-6
• ASME SFA A5.18, ER70S-6
• ABS ER70S-6
• CWB ER49S-6

# Steel Solid Wires

## HB-28
AWS ER70S-6

When your $CO_2$ welding task won't allow for strict cleaning practices, choose HB-28. It's a mild steel electrode that provides sound, porosity-free welds. You'll get excellent weldability with powerful deoxidizers for your work with $CO_2$ and other commercially available shielding gas mixtures.

### Typical applications:
- Construction work
- Farm implement fabrication
- General shop applications with poor fit-up or rusty, oily plates
- Steel castings or forging salvage
- Tanks
- Home projects
- Sheet metal

### Typical wire chemistry (as manufactured):
Carbon..........................................0.08
Manganese....................................1.52
Silicon..........................................0.80
Phosphorus ..................................0.009
Sulphur ........................................0.012

### Typical mechanical properties (AW):
$CO_2$
Tensile Strength (psi) ........86,000 (596 MPa)
Yield Strength (psi)............71,000 (487 MPa)
Elongation % in 2" .............27%

### Typical Charpy V-notch impact values (AW):
Avg. at -20°F (-29°C), $CO_2$......52 ft.lb. (71J)

### Approvals and Conformances:
- AWS A5.18, ER70S-6
- ASME SFA 5.18, ER70S-6

## QUANTUM ARC™ D2
AWS ER80S-D2, ER90S-G

This exceptional quality, high-strength welding wire gives you an X-ray quality weld deposit. You can use it with $CO_2$, $Ar/CO_2$ and $Ar/O_2$ mixtures in situations where porosity is a problem or when you must counter high-sulfur or carbon content in your base metal.

### Typical applications:
- Alloy applications
- Construction equipment
- High-strength welds
- X-ray quality applications

### Typical wire chemistry (as manufactured):
Carbon..........................................0.10
Manganese....................................1.72
Silicon..........................................0.63
Phosphorus ..................................0.008
Sulphur ........................................0.016
Molybdenum ..................................0.49

### Typical mechanical properties (AW):
$CO_2$
Tensile Strength (psi) ........94,000 (643 MPa)
Yield Strength (psi)............80,000 (552 MPa)
Elongation % in 2" .............20%

### Typical Charpy V-notch impact values (AW):
Avg. at -20°F (-29°C), $CO_2$   34 ft.lb. (46J)

### Approvals and Conformances:
- AWS A5.28, ER80S-D2, ER90S-G
- ASME SFA 5.28, ER80S-D2, ER90S-G
- CWB

## FabCO® RXR
AWS E70T-1C

When you're faced with welding through rust, mill scale or light oil, choose the wire specifically designed for the task: FabCO RXR. It's an E70T-1 gas-shielded flux-cored wire that performs beautifully when more deoxidizers are required. It can handle both mild and low alloy steels requiring single-or multi-pass welds. FabCO RXR has a spray type transfer, low spatter and an easily removed moderate volume slag, which completely covers the weld bead. You'll get a weld with deep penetration, a low hydrogen deposit and excellent operator appeal! RXR is designed for use with $CO_2$ shielding gas only.

### Typical applications:
• Mild and low alloy steels
• Single- and multi-pass applications
• Steel structures
• Storage vessels
• Earthmoving equipment
• Heavy fabrications
• Railroad cars including center sills, strikers, bolsters, side sheets, and more

### Typical weld metal properties (Chem Pad):
Carbon..........................................0.06
Manganese ................................1.58
Silicon .........................................0.69
Phosphorus ................................0.015
Sulphur ........................................0.02

### Typical mechanical properties (AW):
Tensile Strength (psi) ........92,000 (634 MPa)
Yield Strength (psi)............77,700 (536 MPa)
Elongation % in 2" .............26.5%

### Typical Charpy V-notch impact values (AW):
Avg. at 0°F (-18°C)............35 ft.lb.(47J)
Avg. at -20°F (-29°C).........22 ft.lb.(30J)

### Recommended welding procedures:

| Dia | Amps | Volts | Electrical Stickout |
|---|---|---|---|
| .045" (1.2 mm) | 150-250 | 21-27 | 1/2"-1" |
| 1/16" (1.6 mm) | 200-375 | 25-29 | 5/8"-1" |
| 5/64" (2.0 mm) | 250-400 | 26-33 | 3/4"-1-1/4" |
| 3/32" (2.4 mm) | 350-550 | 26-36 | 3/4"-1-1/4" |
| 7/64" (2.8 mm) | 500-700 | 30-36 | 3/4"-1-1/4" |
| 1/8" (3.2 mm) | 600-800 | 32-38 | 3/4"-1-1/4" |

### Shielding gas: 100% $CO_2$

### Type of current: DCEP

### Approvals and conformances:
• AWS A5.20, E70T-1C
• ASME SFA 5.20, E701T-1C, E70T-9C
• ABS 100% $CO_2$ 2SA, 2YSA H1O
• CWB E492T-9 H8
• MIL-E-24403/1

## FabCO® TR-70
AWS E70T-1C H8, E70T-9C H8

For a gas-shielded tubular wire with low smoke, low spatter and extremely smooth operator appeal, choose FabCO TR-70. Its deep-penetration, low hydrogen weld deposit is tolerant to rust, mill scale and light oil. Its low-smoke properties make it ideal for light to heavy gauge mild steel and low alloy steels.

### Typical applications:
• Earthmoving equipment
• Heavy fabrications
• Railroad cars
• Steel structures
• Storage vessels

### Typical diffusible hydrogen
(gas chromatography): 6.1ml/100g

### Typical weld metal properties (Chem Pad):
Carbon..........................................0.024
Manganese ................................1.34
Silicon .........................................0.49
Phosphorus ................................0.013
Sulphur ........................................0.010

### Typical mechanical properties (AW):
Tensile Strength (psi) ........85,800 (592 MPa)
Yield Strength (psi)..........74,700 (515 MPa)
Elongation % in 2" .............27%

### Typical Charpy V-notch impact values (AW):
Avg. at 0°F (-18°C)............36 ft.lb.(49J)
Avg. at -20°F (-29°C).........26 ft.lb.(35J)

### Recommended welding procedures:

| Dia. | Amps | Volts | Electrical Stickout |
|---|---|---|---|
| .045" (1.2 mm) | 150-250 | 23-29 | 1/4"-3/4" |
| .052" (1.4 mm) | 150-350 | 24-32 | 1/2"-1" |
| 1/16" (1.6 mm) | 170-350 | 25-34 | 3/4"-1-1/4" |
| 5/64" (2.0 mm) | 250-550 | 26-34 | 3/4"-1-1/4" |
| 3/32" (2.4 mm) | 300-650 | 26-40 | 3/4"-1-1/4" |

### Shielding gas: 100% $CO_2$

### Type of current: DCEP

### Approvals and conformances:
• AWS A5.20, E70T-1C H8, E70T-9C H8
• ASME SFA 5.20 E70T-1C H8, E70T-9C H8
• ABS 100% $CO_2$ E70T-1
• CWB 100% $CO_2$ E492T-9 H8

## FabCO® 85
AWS E70T-5CJ H4, E70T-5MJ H4

You're outside on a construction site. Your arc is exposed to low temperatures and drafts. You need FabCO 85. It's a flux-cored wire with basic type slag and globular type metal transfer.

**Typical applications:**
• Outdoor construction welding
• Welding medium carbon steel
• Welding low alloy high-strength steel
• Welding matching steels
• Heavy equipment

**Typical diffusible hydrogen (gas chromatography):**
100% $CO_2$ 80% Ar/20% $CO_2$
1.10ml/100g 1.61ml/100g

**Typical weld metal properties (Chem Pad):**

|  | 100% $CO_2$ | 80% Ar 20% $CO_2$ |
|---|---|---|
| Carbon | 0.06 | 0.07 |
| Manganese | 1.18 | 1.47 |
| Silicon | 0.60 | 0.75 |
| Phosphorus | 0.009 | 0.010 |
| Sulphur | 0.013 | 0.014 |

**Typical mechanical properties (AW):**

| | | |
|---|---|---|
| Tensile Strength(psi) | 79,000 (545 MPa) | 90,000 (621 MPa) |
| Yield Strength (psi) | 63,000 (434 MPa) | 76,000 (524 MPa) |
| Elongation % in 2" | 29% | 24% |

**Typical Charpy V-notch impact values (AW):**
Avg. at -40°F (-40°C) 45 ft.lb.(61J) 41 ft.lb.(56J)

**Recommended welding procedures:**

| Dia. | Amps | Volts | Electrical Stickout |
|---|---|---|---|
| 5/64" (2.0 mm) | 240-400 | 26-30 | 5/8"-1-1/4" |
| 3/32" (2.4 mm) | 300-500 | 26-32 | 3/4"-1-1/2" |

**Shielding gas:** 100% $CO_2$, 80% Ar/20% $CO_2$

**Type of current:** DCEP

**Approvals and conformances:**
• AWS A5.20, E70T-5CJ H4, E70T-5MJ H4,
• ASME SFA 5.20, E70T-5CJ H4, E70T-5MJ H4
• ABS 100% CO2 E70T-5, 80% Ar/20% CO2 E70T-5
• CWB 100% CO2 E492T-5J H4, 80%Ar/20% CO2 E492T-5MJ H4

## FabCO® Hornet
AWS A5.20: E71T-1C H8, E71T-1M H8, E71T-9C H8, E71T-9M H8,

• Superior penetration profiles
• Promotes high-quality welds
• Easy slag removal and low spatter levels
• Reduces clean-up time, minimizes risk of inclusions
• Good impact strength at low temperatures
• Resists cracking in severe applications
• Low fume generation rate • Increases operator appeal, improves the working environment

**Typical applications:**
• Outdoor construction welding
• Welding medium carbon steel
• Welding low alloy high-strength steel
• Welding matching steels
• Heavy equipment

**Typical diffusible hydrogen (gas chromatography):**
100% $CO_2$ 80% Ar/20% $CO_2$
1.10ml/100g 1.61ml/100g

**Typical weld metal properties (Chem Pad):**

|  | 100% $CO_2$ | 75% Ar 25% $CO_2$ |
|---|---|---|
| Carbon | 0.030 | 0.02 |
| Manganese | 1.29 | 1.52 |
| Silicon | 0.30 | 0.40 |
| Phosphorus | 0.011 | 0.008 |
| Sulphur | 0.005 | 0.004 |

**Typical mechanical properties [Aged 48 hrs@200°F (93°C)]:**

| | | |
|---|---|---|
| Tensile Strength (psi) | 86,000 (6593 MPa) | 93,000 (642 MPa) |
| Yield Strength (psi) | 81,000 (558 MPa) | 89,000 (614 MPa) |
| Elongation % in 2" | 29% | 26% |

**Typical Charpy V-notch impact values (AW):**
Avg. at -40°F (-40°C) 45 ft.lb.(61J) 41 ft.lb.(56J)

**Type of current:** DCEP

**Approvals and conformances:**
• AWS A5.20, E71T-1C H8, E71T-1M H8, E71T-9C H8, E71T-9M H8,
• AWS A5.20M, E491T-1C H8, E491T-1M H8, E491T-9C H8, E491T-9M H8
• ASME SFA 5.20, E71T-1C H8, E71T-1M H8, E71T-9C H8, E71T-9M H8
• ABS, 100% $CO_2$, 3YSA H10, 80% Ar/20%$CO_2$, 3YSA H10
• CWB, 100% $CO_2$, E491T-9-H8, 80% Ar/20%$CO_2$, E491T-9M-H8
• AWS D1.8 Conformance: 0.045" (1.2 mm) & 1/16" (1.6 mm) diameter electrodes with 100% $CO_2$ or 75% Ar/25% $CO_2$ shielding gases

## Excel-Arc 71
AWS E71T-1C, E71T-1M, E71T-9C, E71T-9M H8

A versatile, high-penetrating tubular wire, Excel-Arc 71 is designed to be used with a 100% $CO_2$ or a 75% Ar/25% $CO_2$ gas mixture to make fabrication easier in any position. You'll see a low-hydrogen weld deposit in a spray-type transfer of weld metal, with less smoke, deep penetration and a high-deposition rate. With low spatter, cleanup is a snap and it's great for single- or multi-pass jobs. This wire exceeds the AWS impact strength requirement of 20 ft. lb. at both 0°F and -20°F.

**Typical applications:**
• Low-alloy steels
• Mild steels
• Multi-pass applications
• Single-pass applications

**Typical diffusible hydrogen (gas chromatography):** Less than 7.0ml/100g

**Typical weld metal properties (Chem Pad):**

|  | 100% $CO_2$ | 80% Ar 20% $CO_2$ |
|---|---|---|
| Carbon | 0.021 | 0.022 |
| Manganese | 1.30 | 1.60 |
| Silicon | 0.69 | 0.82 |
| Phosphorus | 0.015 | 0.015 |
| Sulphur | 0.011 | 0.010 |

**Typical mechanical properties (AW):**

| | | |
|---|---|---|
| Tensile Strength (psi) | 87,400 (603 MPa) | 96,000 (662 MPa) |
| Yield Strength (psi) | 79,100 (545 MPa) | 85,800 (592 MPa) |
| Elongation % in 2" | 27.6% | 25.8% |

**Typical Charpy V-notch impact values (AW):**
Avg. at -0°F (-18°C) 70 ft.lb.(95J) 59 ft.lb.(80J)
Avg. at -20°F (-29°C) 51 ft.lb.(69J) 50 ft.lb.(68J)

**Recommended welding procedures:**

| Dia. | Amps | Volts | Electrical Stickout |
|---|---|---|---|
| .035" (0.9 mm) | 140-250 | 20-25 | 3/8"-5/8" |
| .045" (1.2 mm) | 180-280 | 22-28 | 1/2"-3/4" |
| .052" (1.4 mm) | 190-310 | 22-29 | 5/8"-3/4" |
| 1/16" (1.6 mm) | 180-360 | 22-30 | 5/8"-1" |

**Shielding gas:** 100% $CO_2$, 75% Ar/25% $CO_2$

**Type of current:** DCEP

**Approvals and conformances:**
• AWS A5.20, E71T-1C, E71T-1M, E71T-9C, E71T-9M H8
• ASME SFA 5.20, E71T-1C, E71T-1M, E71T-9C, E71T-9M H8
• ABS 75% Ar/25% $CO_2$-3SA, 3YSA H10, 100% $CO_2$ 3SA, 3YSA H10
• Bureau Veritas SA3YM HH
• CWB 100% $CO_2$ E491T-9 H8, 80% Ar/20% $CO_2$ E491T-9M H8
• DNV III Y40M H10
• Lloyd's Register 100% $CO_2$ 3S, 3YS H10

## FabCO® XL®-525
AWS E71T-1M, E71T-12MJ H8

Formula XL-525 is a tubular, all-position wire that is designed for the welding of mild and carbon steels, especially when good impact toughness at subzero temperatures is required. Ideal for single and multi-pass applications, it delivers outstanding welding performance and produces a high quality, X-ray clear weld deposit. Formula XL-525 has outstanding mechanical properties that resemble those of E7018 SMAW electrodes, plus high operator appeal with low fume levels, low spatter and easy slag removal.

**Typical applications:**
• Shipbuilding
• Storage vessels
• Offshore structures
• Earthmoving equipment
• Piping

**Typical diffusible hydrogen (gas chromatography):** 3.38ml/100g

**Typical weld metal properties (Chem Pad):**
80% Ar/20% $CO_2$

| | |
|---|---|
| Carbon | 0.04 |
| Manganese | 1.24 |
| Silicon | 0.29 |
| Nickel | 0.37 |
| Phosphorus | 0.010 |
| Sulphur | 0.015 |

**Typical mechanical properties (AW):**
80% Ar/20% $CO_2$
Tensile Strength (psi) 82,000 (565 MPa)
Yield Strength (psi) 73,000 (503 MPa)
Elongation % in 2" 29%

**Typical Charpy V-notch impact values (AW):**
Avg. at 0°F(-18°C) 100 ft.lb.(136J)
Avg. at -40°F(-40°C) 66 ft.lb.(90J)

**Recommended welding procedures:**

| Dia. | Amps | Volts | Electrical Stickout |
|---|---|---|---|
| .045" (1.2 mm) | 150-300 | 24-31 | 1/2"-1" |
| 1/16" (1.6 mm) | 225-450 | 24-34 | 1/2"-1" |

**Shielding gas:** 75-80% Ar/20-25% $CO_2$

**Type of current:** DCEP

**Approvals and conformances:**
• AWS A5.20 E71T-1M, E71T-12MJ H8,
• ASME SFA 5.20, Class E71T-1M, E71T-12MJ H8
• ABS 80% Ar/20% $CO_2$ 3SA, 3YSA 75% Ar/25% $CO_2$ 3SA, 3YSA
• Bureau Veritas 80% Ar/20% $CO_2$ SA3YM
• CWB 80%Ar/20% $CO_2$ E491T-12M H8
• DNV Grade III Y40 MS
• Lloyd's Register 80%Ar/20%$CO_2$ 3S 3YS H15

## FabCO® XL®-550
AWS E71T-1, E71T-12J H4
.045", .052": AWS E71T-1C, E71T-12CJ H4
1/16": AWS E71T-1C, E71T-12CJ H8

Formula XL-550 is formulated with added deoxidizers to allow you to weld through rust, mill scale and some primers with little or no pre-cleaning. Outstanding, all-position Formula XL-550 is designed to weld mild steels, producing a high-quality, X-ray clear weld deposit that delivers high impact values at low temperatures. Good wet-in action produces a bead contour that's flat to slightly convex with light slag that keeps clean-up time to a minimum.

### Typical applications:
• Ships
• Storage vessels
• Structures
• Earthmoving equipment
• Piping

### Typical diffusible hydrogen
(gas chromatography): Less than 4ml/100g

### Typical weld metal properties (Chem Pad):
100% $CO_2$
Carbon.....................................0.04
Manganese..............................0.67
Silicon.....................................0.16
Phosphorus............................0.008
Sulphur...................................0.013
Nickel......................................0.44

### Typical mechanical properties (AW):
100% $CO_2$
Tensile Strength (psi) ........74,000 (510 MPa)
Yield Strength (psi)............66,000 (455 MPa)
Elongation % in 2" .............28%

### Typical Charpy V-notch impact values (AW):
Avg. at -0°F (-18°C) 83 ft.lb. (113J)
Avg. at -40°F (-40°C) 30 ft.lb. (41J)

### Recommended welding procedures:

| Dia. | Amps | Volts | Electrical Stickout |
|---|---|---|---|
| .045" (1.2 mm) | 195-230 | 23-26 | 1/2"-1" |
| .052" (1.4 mm) | 210-260 | 23-28 | 1/2"-1" |

Shielding gas: 100% $CO_2$

Type of current: DCEP

### Approvals and conformances:
• AWS A5.20, E71T-1C, E71T-12CJ H4
• ASME SFA 5.20, E71T-1
• .045"-.052" AWS E71T-1C, E71T-12CJ H4 1/16" AWS E71T-1C H8, AWS E71T-12CJ H8
• ABS 3SA, 3YSA
• MIL-E-24403/1

## FabCO® 81K2-C
AWS 81T1-K2CJ H8

FabCO 81K2-C is an all-position low alloy flux cored wire. This high performance 100% $CO_2$ electrode is characterized by a flat bead profile, smooth stable arc and low spatter even when welded out of position. The exceptional mechanical properties and low diffusible hydrogen makes this product well suited for the shipbuilding and offshore oil construction market.

### Typical applications:
• Offshore
• Shipyard

### Typical diffusible hydrogen: 3.9ml/100g

### Typical weld metal properties (Chem Pad):
100% $CO_2$
Carbon.........................................0.07
Manganese...................................1.13
Silicon.........................................0.27
Phosphorus.................................0.015
Sulphur........................................0.014
Nickel...........................................1.67

### Typical mechanical properties (AW):
100% $CO_2$
Tensile Strength (psi) ........82,900 (572 MPa)
Yield Strength (psi)............74,800 (516 MPa)
Elongation % in 2" .............26.5%

### Typical Charpy V-notch impact values (AW):
Avg. at -40°F (-40°C) 91 ft.lb. (123J)

### Recommended welding procedures:

| Dia. | Amps | Volts | Electrical Stickout |
|---|---|---|---|
| .045" (1.2 mm) | 150-300 | 23-30 | 1/2"-3/4" |
| 1/16" (1.6 mm) | 175-400 | 23-31 | 1/2"-3/4" |

Shielding gas: 100% $CO_2$

Type of current: DCEP

### Approvals and conformances:
• AWS A5.29, E81T1-K2CJ H8
• ASME SFA 5.29, E81T1-K2CJ
• ABS 100%$CO_2$ 3SA, 3YSA

## FabCO® 115
AWS E110T5-K4C

FabCO 115 is a high strength, flux-cored wire that's comparable to a low alloy E11018M electrode but, with higher deposition rates. It is used primarily for welding A514, A517, HY100 and similar quenched and tempered high-strength, low alloy steels, producing a low hydrogen deposit with basic slag that helps to minimize cracking. FabCO 115 has high impact values at low temperatures and provides you with a modified globular metal transfer. For use with 100% $CO_2$ shielding gas only.

**Typical applications:**
• Mining equipment
• Earthmoving equipment
• Off-the-road vehicles

**Typical weld metal properties (Chem Pad):**
100% $CO_2$
| | |
|---|---|
| Carbon | 0.04 |
| Manganese | 1.50 |
| Silicon | 0.41 |
| Phosphorus | 0.012 |
| Sulphur | 0.014 |
| Chromium | 0.42 |
| Nickel | 2.37 |
| Molybdenum | 0.42 |

**Typical mechanical properties
(Aged 48 hours @ 220°F):**
100% $CO_2$
Tensile Strength (psi) ........113,700 (784 MPa)
Yield Strength (psi)............92,700 (639 MPa)
Elongation % in 2" .............22%

**Typical Charpy V-notch impact values (AW):**
Avg. at -60°F (-51°C) 37 ft.lb. (50J)

**Recommended welding procedures:**

| Dia. | Amps | Volts | Electrical Stickout |
|---|---|---|---|
| .045" (1.2 mm) | 120-220 | 22-27 | 1/2"-1" |
| 1/16" (1.6 mm) | 190-350 | 22-30 | 1/2"-1" |
| 3/32" (2.4 mm) | 290-525 | 25-32 | 3/4"-1-1/4" |

**Shielding gas:** 100% $CO_2$

**Type of current:** DCEP

**Approvals and conformances:**
• AWS A5.29, E110T5-K4C
• ASME SFA 5.29, E110T5-K4C
• ABS 100% $CO_2$ E110T5-K4
• CWB 100% $CO_2$ E110T5-K4 H4, 80% $CO_2$ Ar/20% $CO_2$ E110T5-K4M H4

## Fabshield® 4
AWS E70T-4

Drafts or moderate wind will not affect your weld when you're using this outstanding high deposition, self-shielded flux-cored wire. It's designed specifically to desulfurize the weld metal and to resist cracking. You'll use it in both single and multi-pass applications on mild and medium carbon steels.

**Typical applications:**
• Heavy equipment repair
• Industrial equipment repair
• Machinery fabrication
• Ship equipment

**Typical weld metal properties
(Chem Pad):**
| | |
|---|---|
| Carbon | 0.27 |
| Manganese | 0.73 |
| Silicon | 0.30 |
| Phosphorus | 0.011 |
| Sulphur | 0.005 |
| Aluminum | 1.42 |

**Typical mechanical properties (AW):**
Tensile Strength (psi) ........94,600 (652 MPa)
Yield Strength (psi)............62,600 (432 MPa)
Elongation % in 2" .............24%

**Typical Charpy V-notch impact values:**
Not applicable

**Recommended welding procedures:**

| Dia. | Amps | Volts | Electrical Stickout |
|---|---|---|---|
| 5/64" (2.0 mm) | 290-370 | 29-31 | 1-3/4"-2-1/4" |
| 3/32" (2.4 mm) | 320-450 | 29-34 | 2-1/4"-2-3/4" |
| .120" (3.2 mm) | 450-560 | 28-35 | 2-1/2"-3" |

**Shielding gas:** None required

**Type of current:** DCEP

**Approvals and conformances:**
• AWS A5.20, E70T-4
• ASME SFA 5.20, E70T-4

*For more information: http://www.hobartbrothers.com*

## Fabshield® 7027
AWS E70T-7

When the properties of the physical weld deposit must match the structural weldment application, you'll like the properties of Fabshield 7027. It's designed to give you peak performance at higher amperage and voltage settings while maintaining excellent arc stability and high deposition efficiency. You'll see fast travel speeds with a barium-free slag system that's fast-freezing. It's great for single- and multi-pass welds in flat and horizontal positions for many of your general fabrication needs.

### Typical applications:
• Barges
• General flat weld fabrication
• Structural steel fabrication

### Typical weld metal properties (Chem Pad):
Carbon............................................0.33
Manganese..................................0.28
Silicon.........................................0.05
Phosphorus ................................0.014
Sulphur .......................................0.005
Aluminum.....................................1.3

### Typical mechanical properties (AW):
Tensile Strength (psi) ........92,200 (636 MPa)
Yield Strength (psi)............63,200 (436 MPa)
Elongation % in 2" .............23%

### Typical Charpy V-notch impact values:
Not applicable

### Recommended welding procedures:

| Dia. | Amps | Volts | Electrical Stickout |
|------|------|-------|---------------------|
| 5/64" (2.0 mm) | 240-460 | 23-30 | 1"-2" |
| 3/32" (2.4 mm) | 240-560 | 27-32 | 1"-2" |
| 7/64" (2.8 mm) | 320-600 | 24-32 | 1"-2" |

**Shielding gas:** None required

**Type of current:** DCEN

### Approvals and conformances:
• AWS A5.20, E70T-7
• ASME SFA 5.20, E70T-7
• ABS E70T-7

## Fabshield® 81N1
AWS E71T8-Ni1 J

Fabshield 81N1 is great for a variety of structural and general fabrication applications. This all-position wire is designed for single- or multiple-pass applications requiring high impact toughness at low temperatures. Excellent for vertical down welding on pipe.

### Typical applications:
• Storage piping
• Transportation
• Offshore structures
• Construction
• General fabrication

### Typical weld metal properties (Chem Pad):
Carbon..........................................0.06
Manganese..................................0.76
Silicon.........................................0.08
Phosphorus ................................0.01
Sulphur .......................................0.005
Nickel..........................................0.92
Aluminum.....................................0.78

### Typical mechanical properties (AW):
Tensile Strength (psi) ........76,000 (524 MPa)
Yield Strength (psi)............64,000 (441 MPa)
Elongation % in 2" .............29%

### Typical Charpy V-notch impact values (AW):
Avg. at -40°F (-40°C) 180 ft.lb. (244J)

### Recommended welding procedures:

| Dia. | Amps | Volts | Electrical Stickout |
|------|------|-------|---------------------|
| 5/64" (2.0 mm) | 200-350 | 18-22 | 1" |

**Shielding gas:** None required

**Type of current:** DCEN

### Approvals and conformances:
• AWS A5.29, E71T8-Ni1 J
• ASME SFA 5.29, Class 71T8-Ni1 J
• ABS E71T 8-Ni1J
• EN758: T38 41Ni YN2 H10

## Fabshield® XLR-8
AWS E71T-8JD H8

The Fabshield XLR-8 produces flat weld beads across a broad range of parameters and produces welds with excellent mechanical properties under a wide range of heat inputs. The Fabshield XLR-8 is capable of depositing X-Ray quality welds in all positions.

**Typical applications:**
• Structural steel erection
• Heavy equipment repair
• Ship & barge construction

**Typical weld metal properties (Chem Pad):**
Carbon..........................................0.19
Manganese....................................0.51
Silicon...........................................0.17
Phosphorus ..................................0.009
Sulphur .........................................0.006
Aluminum......................................0.51

**Typical Mechanical Properties
(Aged 48 hr @ 200° F)**
Tensile Strength (psi) ........84,100 (580 MPa)
Yield Strength (psi) .............. 67,600 (466 MPa)
Elongation % in 2" .............25%

**Typical Charpy V-Notch Impact Value (AW):**
Avg. at -20°F (-29°C) 40 ft.lb. (54J)
Avg. at -40°F (-40°C) 31 ft.lb. (42J)

**Recommended welding procedures:**

| Dia. | Amps | Volts | Electrical Stickout |
|------|------|-------|---------------------|
| 1/16" (1.6 mm) | 140-300 | 19-25 | 1" |
| .072" (1.8 mm) | 150-350 | 18-25 | 1" |
| 5/64" (2.0 mm) | 150-350 | 18-25 | 1 1/4" |

**Shielding gas:** None required

**Type of current:** DCEN

**Approvals and conformances**
• AWS E71T-8JD H8
• ASME SFA 5.20 E71T-8JD H8
• ABS 3YSA
• CWB E491T-8J H8

## Fabshield® 21B
AWS E71T-11

You'll find this self-shielded flux-cored wire is easy to use for almost any general purpose application and in any position — flat, horizontal, vertical up and down, and overhead. It's great in single- or multi-pass welds up to 3/4" thick, and particularly well-suited for fillet and lap welds on thin-gauge mild or galvanized steel. Fabshield 21B meets AWS side-bend requirements.

**Typical applications:**
• General fabrication
• Light structurals
• Machinery part fabrication
• Prefab construction
• Railroad car repair
• Short-assembly welds
• Tanks

**Typical weld metal properties (Chem Pad):**
Carbon..........................................0.31
Manganese....................................0.36
Silicon...........................................0.18
Phosphorus ..................................0.014
Sulphur .........................................0.001
Aluminum......................................0.96

**Typical mechanical properties (AW):**
Tensile Strength (psi) ........91,600 (632 MPa)
Yield Strength (psi)............64,900 (448 MPa)
Elongation % in 2" .............22%

**Typical Charpy V-notch impact values:**
Not applicable

**Recommended welding procedures:**

| Dia. | Amps | Volts | Electrical Stickout |
|------|------|-------|---------------------|
| .035" (0.9 mm) | 55-120 | 17-20 | 1/4"-5/8" |
| .045" (1.2 mm) | 80-220 | 13-20 | 1/4"-5/8" |
| 1/16" (1.6 mm) | 110-270 | 14-20 | 1/2"-3/4" |
| .068" (1.8 mm) | 150- 270 | 18-21 | 1/2"-3/4" |
| 5/64" (2.0 mm) | 125-300 | 15-22 | 3/4"-1" |
| 3/32" (2.4 mm) | 200-300 | 18-21 | 3/4"-1" |

**Shielding gas:** None required

**Type of current:** DCEN

**Approvals and conformances:**
• AWS A5.20, E71T-11
• ASME SFA 5.20, E71T-11
• ABS E71T-11
• CWB E491T-11 H8

*For more information: http://www.hobartbrothers.com*

## FabCO® Triple 7

AWS E71T-1C HB

FabCO Triple 7 is designed for the semi-automatic gas shielded welding of carbon steel and some higher strength steels where requirements and conditions do not exceed its capabilities. It is intended for single- and multiple-pass welding in all positions and has a fast-freezing slag that permits the welder to use higher current to deposit more metal faster and still produce a flat bead in all positions. The slag removes easily even from deep groove weldments and spatter is low, so a welder spends more time welding and less time cleaning up. The X-ray quality surpasses the radiographic specifications of AWS A5.20 and ASME SFA 5.20 when welded with the recommended procedures.

**Typical applications:**
• Shipbuilding
• Railcar fabrication
• General plate fabrication
• Heavy gauge sheet metal
• Pressure vessels and certain pipe weldments.

**Typical diffusible hydrogen:** $CO_2$ 4.6 mls/100g

**Typical weld metal properties (Chem Pad):**
Carbon..........................................0.03
Manganese...................................1.27
Silicon .........................................0.56
Phosphorus .................................0.013
Sulphur .......................................0.009

**Typical mechanical properties (AW):**
Tensile Strength (psi) ........90,000 (617MPa)
Yield Strength (psi) ............79,000 (547MPa)
Elongation % in 2" .............27%

**Typical Charpy V-notch impact values:**
0°F (-18°C) 76 ft. lbs. (103J)

**Recommended welding procedures:**

| Dia. | Amps | Volts | Electrical Stickout |
|---|---|---|---|
| .045" | 100-325 | 23-34 | 1/2-3/4" |
| .052" | 125-350 | 22-33 | 1/2-3/4" |
| 1/16" | 150-450 | 23-35 | 1/2-3/4" |

**Type of current:** DCEP

**Approvals and conformances:**
• AWS A5.20, E71T-1C H8
• ASME SFA 5.20, E71T-1M H8
• ABS Grade 2SA, 2YSA
• CWB E491T-1 H8, E491T-1M H8
• DNV II YMS

## FabCO® 811N1

AWS E81T1-Ni1CJ H4, E81T1-Ni1MJ H4

FabCO 811N1 is an all position wire with 1% nickel deposit. Used in applications where low temperature notch toughness is required. Can be used on weathering types of steel where color match is not required.

**Typical applications:**
• High-strength low-alloy steels
• Single and multi-pass welding
• Weathering steels (ASTM A588, A709, etc.)
• Bridge fabrication
• Heavy equipment fabrication
• Structural fabrication
• Shipbuilding

**Typical weld metal properties (Chem Pad):**

| | 100% $CO_2$ | 75% Ar 25% $CO_2$ |
|---|---|---|
| Carbon | 0.03 | 0.022 |
| Manganese | 1.09 | 1.60 |
| Phosphorus | 0.007 | 0.009 |
| Sulphur | 0.005 | 0.008 |
| Silicon | 0.32 | 0.53 |
| Nicke... | 1.01 | 1.00 |

**Typical mechanical properties (AW):**

| | | |
|---|---|---|
| Tensile Strength (psi) ... | 83,000 (572 MPa) | 93,000 (641 MPa) |
| Yield Strength (psi) ....... | 73,000 (503 MPa) | 85,000 (586 MPa) |
| Elongation % in 2" ........ | 26% | 25% |

**Typical Charpy V-notch impact values (AW):**

| | | |
|---|---|---|
| --40°F (-40°C) .............. | 65 ft lbs (88J) | 40 ft lbs (54J) |

**Recommended welding procedures:**

| Dia. | Amps | Volts | Electrical Stickout |
|---|---|---|---|
| .045" | 125-250 | 24-28 | 5/8"-3/4" |
| .052" | 125-300 | 24-27 | 5/8"-3/4" |
| 1/16" | 150-300 | 24-27 | 3/4"-1" |

**Type of current:** DCEP

**Approvals and conformances:**
• AWS A5.29, E81T1-Ni1CJ H4, E81T1-Ni1MJ H4
• AWS A5.29M, E551T1-Ni1CJ H4, E81T1-Ni1MJ H4
• ABS 100% CO2, 3YSA
• CWB, 100% CO2, E551T1-Ni1C-JH8
• CWB, 75-80% Ar/Balance CO2, E551T1-Ni1M-JH8
• AWS D1.8, 75% Ar/25% CO2 (1/16" diameter electrode)

## FabCO® 991K2
AWS E91T1-K2C H8

FabCO 991K2 offers exceptional combination of properties for an all-position wire, with good low temperature toughness combined with tensile strength in the 90,000-110,000 psi range. FabCO 991K2 is characterized by welder appeal, with a smooth stable arc, low smoke and spatter levels. The quick-freezing slag is easily removed and bead geometry in all positions is excellent.

**Typical applications:**
• All-position work with many high strength low alloy steels such as A514, A710, and HY-80.
• It is recommended for single-and multiple-pass welding in all positions with 100% $CO_2$ or 75% Ar/25% $CO_2$ shielding gas.

**Typical diffusible hydrogen:** 3.8 mls/100g

**Typical weld metal properties (Chem Pad):**
100% $CO_2$
Carbon...........................................0.05
Manganese....................................1.04
Silicon...........................................0.19
Phosphorus ...................................0.009
Sulphur .........................................0.014
Molybdenum ..................................0.01
Nickel............................................1.92

**Typical mechanical properties (AW):**
100% $CO_2$
Tensile Strength (psi) ........92,000 (635MPa)
Yield Strength (psi)............80,000 (552MPa)
Elongation..........................27%

**Typical Charpy V-notch impact values (AW):**
0°F (-18°C) 85 ft. lbs. (115J)

**Recommended welding procedures:**

| Dia. | Amps | Volts | Electrical Stickout |
|------|------|-------|---------------------|
| .045" | 150-300 | 23-30 | 1/2" |
| .052" | 175-375 | 23-32 | 1/2" |

**Type of current:** DCEP

**Approvals and conformances:**
• AWS A5.29, E91T1-K2C H8
• ASME SFA 5.29, E91T1-K2M H8
• ABS to AWS E91T1-K2; E91T1-K2M

## FabCO® 911B3
AWS E91T1-B3C H4, E91T1-B3M H4

FabCO 911B3 is suitable for use on materials having a similar composition, such as ASTM A387 or P21/P22 Pipe. Suitable for extended service at elevated temperature. Provides good puddle control and bead contour when welding in all positions. Provides versatility in procedure and application development.

**Typical applications:**
FabCO 911B3 is recommended for single and multiple-pass applications with 75% Ar/25% $CO_2$ shielding gas.

**Typical weld metal properties (Chem Pad):**
100% $CO_2$
Carbon...........................................0.05
Manganese....................................0.59
Silicon...........................................0.26
Phosphorus ...................................0.009
Sulphur .........................................0.010
Chromium ......................................2.32
Molybdenum ..................................0.96

**Typical diffusible hydrogen:** 2.9mls/100g

**Typical mechanical properties (AW):**
100% $CO_2$
Tensile Strength (psi) ........96,000 (662MPa)
Yield Strength (psi)............83,000 (572MPa)
Elongation..........................22%

**Typical Charpy V-notch impact values (AW):**
Not required.

**Recommended welding procedures:**

| Dia. | Amps | Volts | Electrical Stickout |
|------|------|-------|---------------------|
| .045" | 115-325 | 21-30 | 5/8" - 3/4" |
| .052" | 150-425 | 22-31 | 5/8" - 1" |

**Type of current:** ?????

**Approvals and conformances:**
• AW SA5.29,E91T1-B3C H4,E91T1-B3M H4
• AW SA5.29M,E621T1-B3C H4,E621T1-B3M H4
• ASME SFA 5.29,E91T1-B3C H4,E91T1-B3M H4

### FabCO® 101
AWS E101T1-GM

FabCO 101 minimizes the crack sensitivity in quench and tempered low alloy steels such as ASTM A514. Excellent impact properties at low temperatures.

**Typical applications:**
FabCO 101 is recommended for single and multiple-pass applications with 75% Ar/25% $CO_2$ shielding gas.

**Typical diffusible hydrogen:** 4.5mls/100g

**Typical weld metal properties (Chem Pad):**
75% Ar/25% $CO_2$
Carbon..........................................0.04
Manganese....................................1.40
Silicon...........................................0.32
Phosphorus ..................................0.009
Sulphur .........................................0.007
Nickel............................................1.75
Molybdenum..................................0.01

**Typical mechanical properties (AW):**
75% Ar/25% $CO_2$
Tensile Strength (psi) ........103,000 (710MPa)
Yield Strength (psi)............96,000 (662MPa)
Elongation..........................22%

**Typical Charpy V-notch impact values (AW):**
-40°F (-40°C) 70 ft. lbs. (95J)

**Recommended welding procedures:**

| Dia. | Amps | Volts | Electrical Stickout |
|---|---|---|---|
| .045" | 150-300 | 22-28 | 3/4" |
| 1/16" | 175-400 | 22-32 | 3/4"-1" |

**Type of current:** ????

**Approvals and conformances:**
• AWS E101T1-GM
• AWS E691T1-GM
• ASME E101T1-GM

*For more information: http://www.hobartbrothers.com*

# Hard Surfacing Wires

## Hobart FabTuf® 960

With $CO_2$ shielding, FabTuf 960 is the right filler metal when you need a high quality, uniform deposit that's porosity-free. It's ideal for $CO_2$ welding in hard surfacing applications where moderate impact strength and moderate abrasion resistance is required. It is also an excellent choice for metal-to-metal wear resistance applications. During welding, the tubular steel sheath and metal powders of the core fuse together to form alloy steel weld metal with almost no slag. You'll get a deposition efficiency equal to that of solid welding wires. FabTuf 960 can be used for out-of-position welding.

**Typical applications:**
• Coal conveyors
• Conveyor bucket lips
• Dredge parts
• Extruder worms

**Typical weld metal properties (Chem Pad):**
Carbon.........................................0.70
Manganese...................................2.00
Chromium.....................................8.00
Silicon..........................................1.00

**Machinability:** Possible by grinding

**Flame cut:** No

**Hardness:** 55-60 RC

**Wear index:** 35

**Type of current:** DCEP

**Available diameter and recommended operating ranges:**

| Dia. | Amps | Volts |
|---|---|---|
| .045" (1.2 mm) | 120-210 | 20-28 |
| 1/16" (1.6 mm) | 170-310 | 20-28 |

## VertiWear® 600

VertiWear® 600 deposits a multipurpose martensitic steel alloy. It can be used to surface mild and low alloy components subject to moderate abrasive wear and medium to high impact. Excellent operator appeal in all position.

**Typical Applications**
• Coupling boxes
• Dragline chain
• Dredge ladder rolls
• Tiln trunnions
• Mill guides
• Sliding metal parts
• Wobbler ends

**Diameter:** .045", 1/16"

**Polarity:** DCEP

**Gas-Shielded**
75 Ar/25% $CO_2$
or 100% $CO_2$

**Typical Deposit Analysis %**
Carbon.........................................0.40
Manganese...................................0.75
Silicon..........................................0.60
Chromium.................................... 6.50
Molybdenum.................................1.00
Vanadium ....................................0.05
Iron ...........................................Bal.

**Typical Properties**
Abrasion Resistance: Good
Impact Resistance: Very Good
Machinability: Good

**Hardness, as deposited, Rc**
No. of Layers 1020 Steel
1 52
2 56
3-8 57

Flame cutting is difficult.
Magnetic.

*For more information: http://www.hobartbrothers.com*

# Hard Surfacing Wires

## Tube-Alloy® 255-G

Tube-Alloy® 255-G is a small-diameter, gas shielded premium hard surfacing wire that deposits an extremely wear-resistant chromium-carbide overlay. It is designed for overlay on carbon, low alloy, cast iron, and austenitic manganese base metals. It outlasts competitive wires which deposit martensitic deposits 9 to 1.

**Diameter:** .045"

**Polarity:** DCEP

**Gas-shielded:**
98% Ar /2% $O_2$, 75 Ar/25 $CO_2$

**Typical Deposit Analysis %**
Carbon...........................................5.30
Manganese....................................1.00
Silicon...........................................0.40
Chromium....................................18.00
Iron ...........................................Bal.

**Typical Properties**
Abrasion resistance: Excellent
Impact resistance: Poor
Machinability: Grinding is difficult
Thickness: 3 Layers

**Maximum Hardness, as deposited, Rc**

| No. of Layers | 1020 Steel | Manganese Steel |
|---|---|---|
| 1 | 58 | 47 |
| 2 | 61 | 51 |
| 3 | 65 | 54 |

Cannot be flame cut.
Deposit will relief-check crack readily.
Maintains hot hardness to 1250°F.

**Typical Applications:**
- Ammonia knoves
- Augers
- Bucket teeth & lips
- Bulldozer end bits and blades
- Cement chutes
- Coal feeder screws
- Coal pulverizer hammers, rolls and table
- Coke chutes
- Coke pusher shoes
- Conveyor screws
- Crusher jaws and cones
- Cultivator chisels and sweeps
- Dragline buckets
- Dredge cutter heads and teeth
- Dredge pump inlet nozzle & side plates
- Fan blades
- Grizzly bars and fingers
- Gyratory crusher mantles and cones
- Manganese pump shells
- Muller tires
- Ore and coal chutes
- Pipeline ball joints
- Pug mill paddles
- Ripper shanks
- Road rippers
- Scraper blades
- Screw conveyors
- Sheepsfoot tampers
- Sizing screens
- Subsoiler Teeth

## VertiWear® AP

VertiWear® AP is a premium, work-hardening austenitic manganese steel alloy. This flux cored, all-position wire can be used for buildup or overlay on austenitic manganese steel. It can also be used for joining austenitic manganese steel to manganese steel, carbon steel and low alloy steel. The deposit has an excellent impact resistance.

**Diameter:** .045"

**Polarity:** DCEP

**Gas-shielded:** 75% Ar/25% $CO_2$ or 100% $CO_2$

**Typical Deposit Analysis %**
Carbon...........................................0.45
Manganese..................................14.00
Silicon...........................................0.50
Chromium....................................13.50
Nickel...........................................0.50
Iron ...........................................Bal.

**Typical Properties**
Abrasion resistance: Good
Impact resistance: Excellent
Machinability: Fair

**Hardness:**
Work Hardened . . . . . . . . . . . .50-55 Rc

| No. of Layers 1020 Steel | |
|---|---|
| 1 | 24 Rc |
| 2 | 20 Rc |
| 3-8 | 18 RC |

Cannot be flame cut.

**Typical Applications**
- Bucket teeth and lips
- Crusher jaws and cones
- Dragline buckets
- Dredge cutter heads and teeth
- Grizzly bars and fingers
- Gyratory crusher mantles and cones
- Hammer mill hammers
- Hydroelectric turbines
- Impactor crusher bars
- Muller tires
- Pulverizer hammers
- Sizing screens

# Build-Up & Overlay Wires

## Tube-Alloy® 240-O

Tube-Alloy® 240-O deposit is a chromium carbide surfacing alloy. It can be used on components subject to severe abrasive wear and heavy impact. The weld metal has higher toughness than conventional chromium carbide due to fewer stress relief-check cracks.

**Diameter:** .045", 1/16", 7/64"

**Polarity:** DCEP

### Typical Deposit Analysis %
| | |
|---|---|
| Carbon | 3.20 |
| Manganese | 0.80 |
| Silicon | 1.90 |
| Chromium | 15.50 |
| Iron | Bal. |

### Typical Properties
Abrasion resistance: Very good
Impact resistance: Fair
Machinability: Grinding only
Thickness: 3-5 layers maximum

### Hardness, as deposited, Rc
| No. of Layers | 1020 Steel* | 12-14% Manganese |
|---|---|---|
| 1 | 40 | 35 |
| 2 | 48 | 42 |
| 3 | 52 | 50 |

Can be flame cut

Deposit will relief-check crack

### Typical Applications
- Ammonia knives
- Augers
- Bucket teeth & lips
- Bulldozer end bits & blades
- Conveyer screws
- Crusher jaws & cones
- Crusher rolls
- Cultivator chisels & sweeps
- Dragline buckets
- Dredge pump impellers & side plates
- Hammer mill hammers
- Impactor crusher bars
- Manganese pump shells
- Mill guides
- Muller tires
- Pipeline ball joints
- Pulverizer hammers
- Scraper blades
- Screw conveyors
- Sheepsfoot tampers
- Sizing screens

## Tube-Alloy® 255-O

Tube-Alloy® 255-O deposit is a premium high chromium carbide surfacing alloy. It can be used on components subject to extremely severe abrasive wear and moderate impact. It can also be used where high temperature (up to 1250°F) wear resistance is required. The weld metals will stress relief-check crack. Can be run as submerged arc by using MK-N neutral flux.

**Diameter:** 1/16", 7/64"

**Polarity:** DCEP

### Typical Deposit Analysis %
| | |
|---|---|
| Carbon | 4.50 |
| Manganese | 0.90 |
| Silicon | 0.50 |
| Chromium | 26.50 |
| Iron | Bal. |

### Typical Properties
Abrasion resistance: Excellent
Impact resistance: Poor
Machinability: Grinding only
Thickness: 3 Layers Maximum

### Hardness, as deposited, Rc
| No. of Layers | 1020 Steel* | 12-14% Manganese |
|---|---|---|
| 1 | 54 | 48 |
| 2 | 56 | 50 |
| 3 | 58 | 53 |

Cannot be flame cut.
Deposit will relief-check crack readily.
Maintains Hot Hardness to 1250°F.

### Typical Applications
- Ammonia knives
- Augers
- Bucket teeth & lips
- Bulldozer blades
- Bulldozer end bits & blades
- Cement chutes
- Coal feeder screws
- Coal pulverizer hammers, rolls & table
- Coke chutes
- Coke pusher shoes
- Conveyor screws
- Dredge pump inlet nozzle & side plates
- Fan blades
- Grizzly bars & fingers
- Gyratory crusher mantles & cones
- Manganese pump shells
- Muller tires
- Ore & coal chutes
- Pipeline ball joints
- Pug mill paddles
- Ripper shanks
- Road rippers
- Scraper blades
- Screw conveyors
- Sheepsfoot tampers
- Similar to those for Tube-Alloy® 240-O where additional abrasion resistance is required
- Sizing screens
- Subsoiler teeth

# Build-Up & Overlay Wires

## Tube-Alloy® 242-O

Tube-Alloy® 242-O is a self-shielded, flux cored wire that deposits a premium martensitic alloy steel. It has excellent resistance to adhesive (metal-to-metal) wear. The deposit has good resistance to abrasion and impact makes it a versatile overlay alloy. It is designed for use as an overlay on carbon and low alloy steels or as a base of Tube-Alloy Build Up-O. With proper preheating, crackfree deposits can be obtained. Tube-Alloy 242-O should never be used for joining.

**Diameter:** .045", 1/16", 7/64"

**Polarity:** DCEP

### Typical Deposit Analysis %
| | |
|---|---|
| Carbon | 0.25 |
| Manganese | 1.30 |
| Silicon | 0.70 |
| Chromium | 4.00 |
| Molybdenum | 0.50 |
| Iron | Bal. |

### Typical Properties
Abrasion resistance: Good
Impact resistance: Good
Machinable

### Hardness, as deposited, Rc
| No. of Layers | 1020 Steel |
|---|---|
| 1 | 36 |
| 2 | 39 |
| 3 | 42 |

Can be flame cut.
Magnetic.

### Typical Applications
• Carbon steel rolls
• Crane wheels
• Dragline chain
• Frogs & switch points
• Idlers
• Low alloy steel railroad crossovers and rail ends
• Steel shafts
• Tractor rollers

## Tube-Alloy® 244-O

Tube-Alloy® 244-O deposit is a medium alloy carbide steel. It is designed primarily for the automatic rebuilding of dredge pump shells. Deposits do stress relief-check crack.

**Diameter:** 7/64"

**Polarity:** DCEP

### Typical Deposit Analysis %
| | |
|---|---|
| Carbon | 2.50 |
| Manganese | 1.60 |
| Silicon | 2.00 |
| Chromium | 9.00 |
| Copper | 0.50 |
| Iron | Bal. |

### Typical Properties
Abrasion resistance: Very good
Impact resistance: Fair
Machinability: Very Difficult
Thickness: 3-5 Layers Maximum

### Hardness, as deposited, Rc
| No. of Layers | 1020 Steel | 12-14% Mn Steel |
|---|---|---|
| 1 | 34 | 24 |
| 2 | 37 | 33 |
| 3 | 40 | 38 |

Cannot be flame cut.
Slightly Magnetic.
Deposit will relief-check crack.

### Typical Applications
• Dredge Pump Impellers & Side Plates
• Pipeline Ball Joints
• Pump Shells

## Tube-Alloy® A43-O

Tube-Alloy® A43-O deposit is a premium high chromium-columbium carbide surfacing alloy. It can be used on components subject to extremely severe high and low stress abrasive wear and moderate impact. It can also be used where high temperature (up to 1250°F) wear resistance is required. The deposit will stress relief-check crack readily. Can be run as submerged arc by using MK-N neutral flux.

**Diameter:** 1/16", 7/64"

**Polarity:** DCEP

**Typical Deposit Analysis %**

| | |
|---|---|
| Carbon | 5.50 |
| Manganese | 0.20 |
| Silicon | 1.00 |
| Chromium | 22.00 |
| Columbium | 6.50 |
| Iron | Bal. |

**Typical Properties**
Abrasion resistance: Excellent
Impact resistance: Poor
Machinability: Grinding only
Thickness: 3 layers maximum

**Hardness, as deposited, Rc**

| No. of Layers | 1020 Steel | 12-14% Mn Steel |
|---|---|---|
| 1 | 58 | 48 |
| 2-3 | 62 | 56 |

Cannot be flame cut.

**Typical Applications**
• Augers
• Bucket lips & teeth
• Coal feeder screws
• Coal pulverizer rolls & table
• Coke chutes
• Coke pusher shoes
• Conveyor screws
• Dredge cutter heads & teeth
• Dredge pump inlet nozzle & side plates
• Fan blades
• Grizzly bars & fingers
• Muller tires
• Paving agitator screws
• Pipeline ball joints
• Pug mill paddles
• Scraper blades
• Sheepsfoot tampers
• Sizing screws

## Tube-Alloy® Build Up-O

Tube-Alloy® Build Up-O deposit is a low alloy steel. It is designed for build-up on mild and low alloy steels only. The weld metals have good compressive strength and impact resistance, making it an excellent base for more abrasion-resistant alloys. The deposit has excellent resistance to cracking, even in multiple layers, and is within the machinable range.

**Diameter:** .045", 1/16", 7/64"

**Polarity:** DCEP

**Typical Deposit Analysis %**

| | |
|---|---|
| Carbon | 0.12 |
| Manganese | 2.80 |
| Silicon | 0.80 |
| Chromium | 1.20 |
| Iron | Bal. |

**Typical Properties**
Abrasion resistance: Fair
Impact resistance: Very good
Machinability: Excellent

**Hardness, as deposited, Rc**

| No. of Layers | 1020 Steel | 4130 Steel |
|---|---|---|
| 1 | 30 | 36 |
| 2 | 28 | 30 |
| 3 | 25 | 26 |

Can be flame cut.
Magnetic.
Heat Treatable.

**Typical Applications**
• Bucket teeth & lips
• Crane wheels
• Dragline buckets
• Dragline chain
• Dredge ladder rolls
• Gear teeth
• Kiln trunnion
• Mine car wheels
• Spindles
• Steel shafts
• Wobbler ends

*For more information: http://www.hobartbrothers.com*

# Build-Up & Overlay Wires

## Tube-Alloy® 218-O

Tube-Alloy® 218-O is a work hardening austenitic manganese steel alloy. It can be used for build-up or overlay on austenitic manganese steel only. It can also be used for joining austenitic manganese steel to manganese steel. Deposits are extremely tough and work harden rapidly under high impact.

**Diameter:** .045", 1/16", 7/64"

**Polarity:** DCEP

**Typical Deposit Analysis %**
Carbon...........................................1.00
Mamganese...............................15.00
Silicon..........................................0.40
Chromium....................................3.10
Nickel...........................................0.40
Iron ............................................Bal.

**Typical Properties**
Abrasion resistance: Fair
Impact resistance: Excellent
Tensile strength: 120,000 psi
Yield strength: 80,000 psi
Elongation in 2": 32%
Machinability: Difficult

**Hardness:**
As Deposited: 15-22 Rc
Work Hardened: 50-55 Rc

Flame cutting difficult.
Nonmagnetic.

**Typical Applications**
• Bucket teeth
• Crusher jaws & cones
• Dredge pump casings
• Gyratory crusher mantles & cones
• Hammer mill hammers
• Impactor crusher bars
• Manganese steel railroad crossovers & frogs

## Tube-Alloy® AP-O

Tube-Alloy® AP-O deposit is a premium work hardening austenitic manganese steel alloy. It can be used for build-up or overlay on austenitic manganese steel, carbon steel and low alloy steel. It can also be used for joining austenitic manganese steel to manganese steel, carbon steel and low alloy steel. The weld metal has higher toughness than conventional manganese steel weld metal.

**Diameter:** 1/16", 7/64"

**Polarity:** DCEP

**Typical Deposit Analysis %**
Carbon...........................................0.42
Manganese...............................16.50
Silicon..........................................0.30
Chromium..................................13.00
Iron ............................................Bal.

**Typical Properties**
Abrasion resistance: Fair
Impact resistance: Excellent
Tensile strength: 124,000 psi
Yield strength: 83,000 psi
Elongation in 2": 40%
Machinability: Difficult

**Hardness:**
As Deposited: 18-24 Rc
Work Hardened: 50-55 Rc

Cannot be flame cut.
Nonmagnetic.

**Typical Applications**
• Bucket teeth & lips
• Crusher jaws & cones
• Dragline buckets
• Dredge cutter heads & teeth
• Grizzly bars & fingers
• Gyratory crusher mantles & cones
• Hammer mill hammers
• Hydroelectric turbines
• Impactor crusher bars
• Muller tires
• Pulverizer hammers
• Similar to those for Tube-Alloy® 218-O, especially where the base metal verification is questionable or where contamination may be an issue
• Sizing screens

*For more information: http://www.hobartbrothers.com*

## FabCOR® Edge™ D2
AWS E90C-D2

FabCOR Edge is a low alloy metal cored wire designed for welding mild and high strength low alloy steels. Produces .5% Mo weld deposit.

**Typical applications:**
- High-strength low-alloy steels
- Single or multiple-pass welding
- Pressure vessels
- Automated and mechanized applications

**Typical weld metal properties (Chem Pad):**
98% Ar/2% $O_2$
Carbon..........................................0.05
Manganese....................................1.50
Silicon...........................................0.50
Phosphorus ..................................0.009
Sulphur.........................................0.012
Copper..........................................0.05
Molybdenum .................................0.50

**Typical mechanical properties (AW):**
98% Ar/2% $O_2$
Tensile Strength (psi) ........98,000
Yield Strength (psi)............90,000
Elongation..........................25%

**Typical Charpy V-notch impact values (AW):**
-20°F (-29°C) 55 ft. lbs. (675J)

**Recommended welding procedures:**
Electrical

| Dia. | Amps | Volts | Stickout |
|------|------|-------|----------|
| .045" | 200-350 | 25-28 | 5/8-3/4" |
| .052" | 250-400 | 26-29 | 3/4"-1" |
| 1/16" | 300-450 | 26-29 | 1" |

**Type of current:** DCEP

**Approvals and conformances:**
- AWS A5.28, E90C-D2

## FabCOR® 90
AWS E90C-K3 H4

FabCOR 90 is a low alloy metal cored wire designed for welding high-strength steels. It can be used for both single and multipass welding with either 75-95% Ar/balance $CO_2$ shielding gas.

**Typical applications:**
- Ideal for castings, pressure vessels and other applications associated with building ships and offshore platforms.

**Product characteristics:**
- Excellent wetting characteristics.
- High tensile strength electrode
- High deposition rates possible at low heat inputs
- Can be used with standard CV equipment
- All-position capability when using pulsed-spray transfer

**Typical weld metal properties (Chem Pad):**
75% Ar/25% $CO_2$
Carbon..........................................0.06
Manganese....................................1.18
Silicon...........................................0.25
Sulphur.........................................0.012
Phosphorus ..................................0.009
Nickel............................................1.84
Chromium......................................0.08
Molybdenum ..................................0.34
Vanadium......................................0.00
Copper..........................................0.06

**Typical diffusible hydrogen:** 2.3mls/100g

**Typical mechanical properties (AW):**
75% Ar/25% $CO_2$
Tensile Strength (psi) ........102,000
Yield Strength (psi)............94,000
Elongation..........................23%

**Typical Charpy V-notch impact values (AW):**
-60°F (-50°C) 71 ft. lbs. (96J)

**Recommended welding procedures:**

| Dia. | Amps | Volts | Deposition Rate(lb/hr) |
|------|------|-------|------------------------|
| .045" | 200-350 | 27-30 | 5.9 - 15.2 |

**Approvals and conformances:**
- AWS A5.28, E90C-K3 H4
- AWS A5.28M, E62C-K3 H4
- ASME SFA 5.28, E90C-K3 H4

# Metal Cored Wires

## FabCOR® 100
AWS E100C-K3

FabCOR 100 is a low alloy steel metal cored welding electrode designed to produce weld metal with a minimum of 100 ksi tensile strength. In addition to high tensile strength, the weld metal has excellent low temperature toughness to -60°C. FabCOR100 produces these properties over a wide heat input range. Like most metal cored wires, Metalloy 100 has low diffusible hydrogen levels below 4 ml/100g.

### Product characteristics:
- Single or multi-pass welding of high strength low alloy steels, such as A514, A517, T-1, HY-80, HSLA A80, A710 and many others.
- Higher deposition rates compared to solid wire.
- Designed for $Ar/CO_2$ shielding gas mixtures containing up to 10% $CO_2$.
- Shielding gas mixtures containing more than 10% $CO_2$ may be used but will result in tensile strength below 100 ksi.

### Typical weld metal properties (Chem Pad):
90% Ar/10% $CO_2$

| | |
|---|---|
| Carbon | 0.07 |
| Manganese | 1.50 |
| Silicon | 0.38 |
| Nickel | 1.58 |
| Molybdenum | 0.34 |

### Typical mechanical properties (AW):
90% Ar/10% $CO_2$

| | |
|---|---|
| Tensile Strength (psi) | 113,300 |
| Yield Strength (psi) | 103,300 |
| Elongation | 21% |

### Typical Charpy V-notch impact values (AW):
-60°F (-51°C) 49 ft. lbs. (66J)

### Recommended welding procedures:

| Dia. | Amps | Volts | Deposition Rate(lb/hr) |
|---|---|---|---|
| .045" | 200-350 | 27-35 | 5.9 - 15.2 |
| .052" | 250-400 | 28-34 | 9.0-21.5 |
| 1/16" | 300-450 | 28-34 | 11.2 - 20.9 |

### Approvals and conformances:
- AWS A5.28, E100C-K3

## FabCOR® 86R
AWS E70C-6M H4

Smooth and consistent, this metal-cored gas shielded wire gives you the high deposition rates of a flux-cored wire along with the high efficiency of a solid wire. With its metal powdered core and spray transfer, deposition rates in excess of 20 pounds per hour and deposition efficiencies of 95 percent and greater can be obtained. And you get the minimized spatter, fume and slag that high production environments demand.

### Typical applications:
- Automated or robotic welding
- Earthmoving equipment
- Railcars
- Steel structures
- Storage vessels

### Typical diffusible hydrogen (gas chromatography):
Less than 4.0ml/100g

### Typical weld metal properties (Chem Pad):

| | 75% Ar 25% $CO_2$ | 90% Ar 10% $CO_2$ |
|---|---|---|
| Carbon | 0.057 | 0.042 |
| Manganese | 1.58 | 1.64 |
| Silicon | 0.75 | 0.79 |
| Phosphorus | 0.010 | 0.012 |
| Sulphur | 0.018 | 0.019 |

### Typical mechanical properties (AW):

| | | |
|---|---|---|
| Tensile Strength(psi) | 87,500 | 90,600 |
| Yield Strength(psi) | 75,300 | 77,100 |
| Elongation % in 2" | 29% | 28% |

### Typical Charpy V-notch impact values (AW):
Avg. at -20°F (-29°C) ..... 72 ft.lb.     62 ft.lb.

### Recommended welding procedures:

| Dia. | Amps | Volts | Electrical Stickout |
|---|---|---|---|
| .045" (1.2 mm) | 75-325 | 15-35 | 1/2"-3/4" |
| .052" (1.4 mm) | 100-380 | 16-35 | 1/2"-1" |
| 1/16" (1.6 mm) | 150-450 | 17-35 | 1/2"-1" |
| 3/32" (2.4 mm) | 350-550 | 26-37 | 3/4"-1-1/4" |

### Shielding gas:
75% Ar/25% $CO_2$ or higher argon gas mixtures

### Type of current: DCEP

### Approvals and conformances:
- AWS A5.18, E70C-6M H4
- ASME SFA 5.18, E70C-6M H4
- ABS 80% Ar/20% $CO_2$ 3SA, 3YSA
- Bureau Veritas 80% Ar/20% $CO_2$ SA3YM
- CWB E491C-6M H4
- DNV IIY40 MS
- Lloyd's Register 3S, 3Y40S H15

*For more information: http://www.hobartbrothers.com*

# Metal Cored Wires

## FabCOR® Edge™
AWS E70C-6M H4

FabCOR Edge is a metal-cored wire with fewer silicon islands than other metal-cored wires. On clean material, weld bead toe lines are almost completely free of silicon deposits. The weld bead face is virtually free from silicon island deposits. Together with exceptional low spatter rates, Edge will save time and money spent cleaning prior to painting, coating, or plating. The recommended shielding gas is a mixture of argon and carbon dioxide, with a minimum of 75% argon and a maximum of 95% argon. Arc characteristics improve with richer argon gases while spatter and fume levels decrease.

### Typical applications:
• Recommended for single and multi-pass welding in both the flat and horizontal positions.
• Robotic and automated welding
• Non-alloyed and fine grain steels
• Heavy equipment
• Agriculture
• Transportation
• Mining

### Typical diffusible hydrogen (gas chromatography):
1.5 ml/100 g (75% AR/ 25% $CO_2$)
2.10 ml/100 g (90% AR/ 10% $CO_2$)

### Typical weld metal properties (Chem Pad):

|  | 75% Ar 25% $CO_2$ | 90% Ar 10% $CO_2$ |
|---|---|---|
| Carbon | 0.05 | 0.05 |
| Manganese | 1.33 | 1.50 |
| Silicon | 0.63 | 0.72 |
| Phosphorus | 0.006 | 0.010 |
| Sulphur | 0.007 | 0.012 |
| Nickel | 0.42 | 0.42 |

### Typical mechanical properties (AW):
| | | |
|---|---|---|
| Tensile Strength (psi) | 91,000 | 97,000 |
| Yield Strength (psi) | 81,000 | 87,000 |
| Elongation % in 2" | 25% | 22% |

### Typical Charpy V-notch impact values (AW):
| | | |
|---|---|---|
| Avg. at 0°F (-20°C) | 50 ft.lb. | 56 ft.lb. |
| Avg. at -20°F (-29°C) | 38 ft.lb. | 47 ft.lb. |

### Recommended welding procedures:

| Dia. | Amps | Volts | Electrical Stickout |
|---|---|---|---|
| .045" (1.2 mm) | 200-375 | 25-30 | 5/8"-3/4" |
| .052" (1.4 mm) | 250-400 | 24-30 | 3/4"-1" |
| 1/16" (1.6 mm) | 250-450 | 25-32 | 3/4"-1" |

**Shielding gas:** 75-95% Ar/balance $CO_2$

**Type of current:** DCEP

## FabCOR® 1100
AWS E110C-K4

A 110,000 psi tensile, high performance metal cored wire for use with high strength, low alloy steels such as ASTM 514, HY-100 and T1 steels. Formulated to have low smoke and fume levels while maintaining excellent chemical and mechanical properties. Diffusible hydrogen levels will be less than 4ml/100g of deposited weld metal.

### Typical applications:
• Single or multiple pass applications for welding steels requiring a minimum 110,000 psi tensile strength and where low temperature impact values are required.
• High-strength low alloy steels, quench and temper steels, single or multi-pass welding, castings, heavy equipment, shipbuilding.

### Typical weld metal properties (Chem Pad):

|  | 75% Ar 25% $CO_2$ | 90% Ar 10% $CO_2$ |
|---|---|---|
| Carbon | 0.07 | 0.13 |
| Manganese | 1.52 | 1.50 |
| Silicon | 0.52 | 0.50 |
| Sulfur | 0.007 | 0.005 |
| Phosphorus | 0.004 | 0.003 |
| Nickel | 1.92 | 1.84 |
| Chromium | 0.18 | 0.24 |
| Molybdenum | 0.47 | 0.46 |

### Typical mechanical properties (AW):
| | | |
|---|---|---|
| Tensile Strength (psi) | 118,000 | 128,000 |
| Yield Strength (psi) | 105,000 | 116,000 |
| Elongation % in 2" | 19% | 17% |

### Typical Charpy V-notch impact values (AW):
| | | |
|---|---|---|
| Avg. at -60°F (-50°C) | 43 ft.lb. | 28 ft.lb. |

### Recommended welding procedures:

| Dia. | Amps | Volts | Electrical Stickout |
|---|---|---|---|
| .045" (1.2 mm) | 200-350 | 24-29 | 5/8"-3/4" |
| 1/16" (1.6 mm) | 250-450 | 26-30 | 3/4"-1" |

**Shielding Gas:** 75-95% Ar/Balance $CO_2$

**Type of current:** DCEP

### Approvals and conformances:
• AWS A5.28, E110C-K4
• AWS A5.28M, E76C-K4
• ASME SFA 5.28, E110C-K4
• CWB, 75-95% Ar/Balance $CO_2$, E76C-K4-H4

### Approvals and conformances:
• AWS A5.18, E70C-6M H4
• AWS A5.18M, E48C-6M H4
• ASME SFA 5.18, E70C-6M H4
• ABS, 80% Ar/20% $CO_2$, 3YSA

• CWB, 75-95% Ar/Balance $CO_2$, E491C-6MJ-H4 (1.2 mm diameter electrode only)
• CWB, 75-95% Ar/Balance $CO_2$, E492C-6MJ-H4 (1.4 - 1.6 mm diameter electrodes only)

## FabCOR® 702
AWS E70C-6C

FabCOR 702 is a metal-cored gas shielded wire which combines the high deposition rates of a flux cored wire with the high efficiencies of a solid wire. Formulated to weld with $CO_2$ shielding gas, FabCOR 702 as compared to solid wire will improve productivity through increased deposition rates and higher travel speeds. This metal cored wire is designed for single and multi-pass welding of mild steels. It is particularly well suited for high production and automatic applications where Argon $CO_2$ shielding gas is not available.

**Typical applications:**
• Shipbuilding
• Railcar
• General fabrication

**Typical diffusible hydrogen:**
2.5 ml/100 g (100% $CO_2$)

**Typical undiluted weld metal chemistry:**
100% $CO_2$
Carbon..........................................0.09
Manganese..................................1.30
Silicon..........................................0.56
Phosphorus.................................0.011
Sulfur...........................................0.018

**Typical mechanical properties:**
Tensile Strength (psi) ........85,500
Yield Strength (psi)............69,600
Elongation % in 2" .............24.4

**Typical Charpy V-notch impact values:**
Avg. at 0°F (-18°C)..........57 ft.lb.
Avg. at -20°F (-29°C).........54 ft.lb.

**Recommended welding procedures:**

| Dia. | Amps | Volts | Electrical Stickout |
|------|------|-------|---------------------|
| .045" (1.2 mm) | 200-350 | 29-36 | 5/8"-1/8" |
| .052" (1.4 mm) | 250-400 | 29-36 | 5/8"-1/8" |
| 1/16" (1.6 mm) | 300-460 | 30-37 | 3/4"-1/4" |
| 5/64" (2.0 mm) | 415-535 | 30-36 | 1"-1/4" |
| 3/32" (2.4 mm) | 480-605 | 29-36 | 1"-1/4" |

**Shielding Gas:** 100% $CO_2$

**Type of current:** DCEP

**Approvals and conformances:**
• AWS A5.18, E70C-6C
• ABS (3Y)

## FabCOR® 80B2
E80C-B2

FabCOR 80B2 deposits a chemistry similar to that found in 1 1/4 Cr and 1/2 Mo steels. It is used to weld these steels that must maintain high tensile strengths when subject to high service temperatures and creep resistance is required.

**Typical applications:**
• Fabrication and maintenance of boilers and associated piping. For the welding of 1 1/4 Cr and 1/2 MO steels

**Typical weld metal properties (Chem Pad):**
98% Ar/2% $CO_2$
Carbon..........................................0.08
Manganese..................................0.73
Silicon..........................................0.47
Phosphorus.................................0.009
Sulphur........................................0.011
Chromium....................................1.40
Molybdenum................................0.47

**Typical mechanical properties (AW):**
98% Ar/2% $CO_2$
Tensile Strength (psi) ........107,000
Yield Strength (psi)............92,000
Elongation % in 2" .............22%

**Typical Charpy V-notch impact values:**
Not Required

**Recommended welding procedures:**

| Dia. | Amps | Volts | WFS IPM |
|------|------|-------|---------|
| .045" (1.2 mm) | 200-350 | 20-36 | 260-570 |

**Shielding Gas:** 95-99% Ar/Balance $CO_2$

**Type of current:** DCEP

**Approvals and conformances:**
• AWS A5.28: E80C-B2

## FabCOR Edge™ Ni1
AWS E80C-ni1 H4

FabCOR Edge Ni1 is a metal-cored wire designed for single or multi-pass welding of nickelmolybdenum steels. This wire also incorporates patented formulation to reduce silicon island formation. Weld bead toe lines and weld face are almost completely free of silicon deposits, eliminating cleanup time and effort. The remaining islands of silicon are almost self-peeling. With exceptionally low spatter rates, FabCOR Edge Ni1 will save time and money spent cleaning prior to painting, coating, or plating.

### Typical applications:
• Welding castings, equipment and applications requiring touhness at sub-zero temperatures.
• Suitable for joining HSLA weathering steels in structural construction applications where color match is not required.

### Typical diffusible hydrogen (gas chromatography):
2.05ml/100gr (75% Ar/ 25% $CO_2$)

### Typical weld metal properties (Chem Pad):
75% Ar/25% $CO_2$

| | |
|---|---|
| Carbon | 0.05 |
| Manganese | 1.38 |
| Silicon | 0.65 |
| Phosphorus | 0.011 |
| Sulphur | 0.013 |
| Nickel | 1.0 |

### Typical mechanical properties (AW):
75% Ar/25% $CO_2$

| | |
|---|---|
| Tensile Strength (psi) | 92,000 |
| Yield Strength (psi) | 81,000 |
| Elongation % in 2" | 25% |

### Typical Charpy V-notch impact values (AW):
-20°F (-29°C) .................... 48 ft. lbs. (65J)

### Recommended welding procedures:

| Dia. | Amps | Volts | Electrical Stickout |
|---|---|---|---|
| .045"(1.2 mm) | 200-400 | 27-35 | 5/8±1/8" |
| 1/16"(1.6 mm) | 275-500 | 29-37 | 1"±1/4" |

**Shielding Gas:** 75-95% Ar/Balance $CO_2$

**Type of current:** DCEP

### Approvals and conformances:
• AWS A5.28, E80C-Ni1 H4
• AWS A5.28M, E55C-Ni1 H4
• ASME SFA 5.28, E80C-Ni1 H4
• CWB, 75-95% Ar/Balance $CO_2$, 95-99% Ar/ Balance $O_2$, E55C-Ni1-H8

## FabCOR® 80D2
AWS E90C-D2

Developed for high strength, low alloy steels found in heavy equipment or structural parts.

### Typical applications:
• Single or multiple pass welding with 95% Argon/5% Oxygen
• Heavy equipment
• Structural components

### Typical weld metal properties (Chem Pad):

| | 90% Ar 10% $CO_2$ | 95% Ar 5% $O_2$ |
|---|---|---|
| Carbon | 0.08 | 0.08 |
| Manganese | 1.80 | 1.34 |
| Silicon | 0.66 | 0.53 |
| Phosphorus | 0.005 | 0.003 |
| Sulphur | 0.008 | 0.006 |
| Molybdenum | 0.50 | 0.50 |
| Copper | 0.02 | 0.02 |

### Typical mechanical properties (AW):

| | | |
|---|---|---|
| Tensile Strength(psi) | 106,000 | 105,000 |
| Yield Strength(psi) | 98,000 | 96,000 |
| Elongation % in 2" | 19% | 17% |

### Typical Charpy V-notch impact values (AW):
Avg. at -20°F (-29°C) .... 42 ft.lb.    40 ft.lb.

### Recommended welding procedures:

| Dia. | Amps | Volts | Electrical Stickout |
|---|---|---|---|
| .035" (0.9 mm) | 150-250 | 26-28 | 5/8" |
| .045" (1.2 mm) | 200-350 | 24-29 | 5/8"-3/4" |
| .052" (1.4 mm) | 250-400 | 25-30 | 3/4"-1" |
| 1/16" (1.6 mm) | 250-450 | 24-29 | 3/4"-1" |

### Shielding Gas:
95-99% Argon (Ar)/Balance $O_2$
75-95% Argon (Ar)/Balance $CO_2$

### Type of current: DCEP

### Approvals and conformances:
• AWS A5.28, E90C-D2
• AWS A5.28M, E62C-D2
• ASME SFA 5.28, E90C-D2

# Metal Cored Wires

## FabCOR® 90
AWS E90C-K3 H4

Used in the welding of higher strength steels.

**Typical applications:**
- Single or multiple pass applications with a 75-95% Argon/Balance $CO_2$
- Castings
- Pressure vessels
- Shipbuilding
- Offshore platforms

**Typical diffusible hydrogen (gas chromatography):**
2.33 ml/100 g (75% Ar/ 25% $CO_2$)

**Typical weld metal properties (Chem Pad):**

|  | 75% Ar 25% $CO_2$ | 90% Ar 10% $CO_2$ |
|---|---|---|
| Carbon | 0.06 | 0.06 |
| Manganese | 1.19 | 1.41 |
| Silicon | 0.25 | 0.31 |
| Sulphur | 0.012 | 0.012 |
| Phosphorus | 0.009 | 0.006 |
| Nickel | 1.84 | 1.83 |
| Chromium | 0.08 | 0.08 |
| Molybdenum | 0.34 | 0.34 |
| Vanadium | 0.00 | 0.01 |
| Copper | 0.06 | 0.06 |

**Typical mechanical properties (AW):**

| | | |
|---|---|---|
| Tensile Strength (psi) | 102,000 | 110,000 |
| Yield Strength (psi) | 94,000 | 104,000 |
| Elongation % in 2" | 23% | 22% |

**Typical Charpy V-notch impact values (AW):**
Avg. at -50°F (-45°C)..... 44 ft.lb.    61 ft.lb.

**Recommended welding procedures:**

| Dia. | Amps | Volts | Electrical Stickout |
|---|---|---|---|
| .045" (1.2 mm) | 200-350 | 27-30 | 5/8"-3/4" |
| .052" (1.4 mm) | 250-400 | 27-31 | 3/4" |
| 1/16"(1.6 mm) | 300-450 | 29-31 | 1" |

**Shielding Gas:** 75-95% Ar/Balance $CO_2$

**Type of current:** DCEP

**Approvals and conformances:**
- AWS A5.28, E90C-K3 H4

## FabCOR® 80N2
AWS E80C-Ni2

Metalloy 80N2 is a metal-cored low alloy that is designed for the single– or multi-pass welding of structures where high Charpy-impact values are required at sub-zero temperatures. This higher nickel alloy product offers superior mechanical properties when used with 98% Ar/2% $O_2$ or 75% Ar/25% $CO_2$ shielding gas and is appropriate for the offshore oil platforms, shipbuilding, and other applications where good toughness is desired.

**Typical applications:**
- Single or multiple pass applications with a 98% Argon/2% $O_2$, or 75% Argon/25% $CO_2$
- Offshore platforms
- Shipbuilding

**Typical weld metal properties (Chem Pad):**

|  | 98% Ar 2% $O_2$ | 75% Ar 25% $CO_2$ |
|---|---|---|
| Carbon | 0.04 | 0.03 |
| Manganese | 1.09 | 0.77 |
| Silicon | 0.34 | 0.28 |
| Nickel | 2.26 | 2.23 |

**Typical mechanical properties (AW):**

| | | |
|---|---|---|
| Tensile Strength (psi) | 90,000 | 78,200 |
| Yield Strength (psi) | 77,000 | 65,800 |
| Elongation % in 2" | 26% | 26% |

**Typical Charpy V-notch impact values (AW):**
Avg. at -50°F (-46°C)..... – 38 ft.lb.
Avg. at -80°F (-62°C)..... 48 ft.lb. –

**Recommended welding procedures:**

| Dia. | Amps | Volts | WFS IPM |
|---|---|---|---|
| .045" (1.2 mm) | 200-350 | 27-35 | 240-570 |

**Shielding Gas:**
98% Argon/2% $O_2$
75% Argon/25% $CO_2$

**Type of current:** DCEP

**Approvals and conformances:**
- AWS A5.28, E80C-Ni2

The information contained or otherwise referenced herein is presented only as "typical without guarantee or warranty, and Hobart expressly disclaims any liability incurred from any reliance thereon. Typical data are obtained when welded and tested in accordance with AWS specification. Other tests and precedures may produce different results. No data is to be construed as a recommendation for any welding condition or technique not contolled by Hobart.

# Metal Cored Wires/Hard Surfacing

## FabCOR® 90
AWS E90C-K3 H4

FabCOR® 90 is used in the welding of higher strength steels.

**Typical applications:**
- Single or multiple pass applications with a 75-95% Ar /Balance $CO_2$
- Castings
- Pressure vessels
- Shipbuilding
- Offshore platforms

**Typical diffusible hydrogen (gas chromatography):**
2.33 ml/100 g (75% Ar/ 25% $CO_2$)

**Typical weld metal properties (Chem Pad):**

|  | 75% Ar 25% $CO_2$ | 90% Ar 10% $CO_2$ |
|---|---|---|
| Carbon | 0.06 | 0.06 |
| Manganese | 1.19 | 1.41 |
| Silicon | 0.25 | 0.31 |
| Sulphur | 0.012 | 0.012 |
| Phosphorus | 0.009 | 0.006 |
| Nickel | 1.84 | 1.83 |
| Chromium | 0.08 | 0.08 |
| Molybdenum | 0.34 | 0.34 |
| Vanadium | 0.00 | 0.01 |
| Copper | 0.06 | 0.06 |

**Typical mechanical properties (AW):**

| | | |
|---|---|---|
| Tensile Strength(psi) | 102,000 | 110,000 |
| Yield Strength(psi) | 94,000 | 104,000 |
| Elongation % in 2" | 23% | 22% |

**Typical Charpy V-notch impact values (AW):**
Avg. at -60°F (-51°C) ..... 71 ft.lb.    23 ft.lb.

**Recommended welding procedures:**

| Dia. | Amps | Volts | Electrical Stickout |
|---|---|---|---|
| .045" (1.2 mm) | 200-350 | 27-30 | 5/8"-3/4" |

**Shielding gas:**
75-90% Ar/Balance $CO_2$

**Type of current:** DCEP

**Approvals and conformances:**
- AWS A5.28, E90C-K3 H4

## Tube-Alloy® Build Up-G

Tube-Alloy® Build Up-G is a gas shielded, metal cored wire designed for build-up on carbon and low alloy steels. The weld metals have good compressive strength and impact resistance, making them excellent bases for more abrasion-resistant alloys.

**Typical Applications:**
- Bucket teeth & lips
- Crane wheels
- Dragline buckets
- Dragline chain
- Dredge ladder rolls
- Gear teeth
- Kiln trunnions
- Mine car wheels
- Spindles
- Steel shafts
- Wobbler ends

**Typical Deposit Analysis %:**

| | |
|---|---|
| Carbon | 0.26 |
| Mnanganese | 1.73 |
| Silicon | 0.32 |
| Chromium | 1.85 |
| Iron | Bal. |

**Typical Properties:**
Abrasion resistance: Fair
Impact resistance: Very good
Machinability: Good
Hardness: 25 Rc

Can be flame cut.
Magnetic.

**Diameter:** .045", 1/16"

**Shielding gas:** 75% Ar/25 $CO_2$ or 100% $CO_2$

**Type of current:** DCEP

*For more information: http://www.hobartbrothers.com*

# Metal Cored Wires/Hard Surfacing

## Tube-Alloy® 258-G

Alloy® 258-G is a metal-cored, gas shielded wire which deposits a sound hot work tool steel alloy of the AISI H-12 type. It is extremely resistant to thermal shock and erosion at working temperatures. The alloy has good dimensional stability and uniform heat-treatment response, making it ideally suited for fabrication, modification, and repair of dies and other tool steel parts.

**Typical Applications:**
• Clean out rings
• Die holders
• Dummy blocks
• Extrusion dies
• Forming dies
• Forging dies
• Gripper dies
• Guide rolls
• Header dies
• Hot forming dies
• Mandrels
• Swaging dies

**Typical Deposit Analysis %:**
Carbon.........................................0.40
Manganese..................................1.00
Si licon........................................0.55
Chromium....................................5.00
Molybdenum...............................1.45
Tungsten......................................1.25
Vanadium ...................................0.40
Iron ...........................................Bal.

**Typical Properties:**
Abrasion Resistance: Good
Impact Resistance: Good
Nonmachinable in as-welded condition: Grinding only

**Hardness, as deposited, RC**

| No. of Layers | A36 Plate |
|---|---|
| 1 | 52 |
| 2 | 53 |
| 3 | 57 |
| Temp. | Typical Hardness |
| 950°F | 54 |

Flame cutting difficult.
Good resistance to softening at elevated temp.
Heat treatable.
Good dimensional stability.

**Diameter:** .045", 1/16"

**Shielding gas:** 75% Ar/25 $CO_2$ or 100% $CO_2$

**Type of current:** DCEP

# Filler Metal Guide for Welding Aluminum

| Base Metal to Base Metal | 1060 1100 3003 Alclad 3003 | 2219 A201.0 | 3004 Alclad 3004 | 5005 5050 | 5052 | 5083 5456 |
|---|---|---|---|---|---|---|
| 356.0 A356.0 357.0 A357.0 359.0 443.0 A444.0 | 4043 | 4145 | 4043 | 4043 | 4043 | 5356 |
| 354.0 C335.0 | 4145 | 4145 | 4145 | 4145 | 4043 | NR |
| 7005 | 5356 | 4145 | 5356 | 5356 | 5356 | 5556 |
| 6005 6005A 6061 Alclad 6061 6063 6082 6351 | 4043 | 4145 | 5356 | 4043 5356 | 4043 5356 | 5356 |
| 5454 | 4053 | 4043 | 5356 | 5356 | 5356 | 5356 |
| 5154 5254 | 4043 | NR | 5356 | 5356 | 5356 | 5356 |
| 5086 514.0 535.0 | 5356 | NR | 5356 | 5356 | 5356 | 5356 |
| 5083 5456 | 5356 | NR | 5356 | 5356 | 5356 | 5183 5556* |
| 5052 | 4043 | 4043 | 4043 | 4043 5356 | 5356 | |
| 5005 5050 | 4043 | 4145 | 4043 | 4043 5356 | | |
| 3004 Alclad 3004 | 4043 | 4145 | 4043 | | | |
| 2219 A201.0 | 4145 | 2319 | | | | |
| 1060 1100 3003 Alclad 3003 | 1100 | | | | | |

# Filler Metal Guide for Welding Aluminum

| 5086 14.0 35.0 | 5154 5254 | 5454 | 6005 6005A 6061 Alclad 6061 6063 6082 6351 | 7005 | 354.0 C335.0 | 356.0 A356.0 357.0 A357.0 359.0 443.0 A444.0 |
|---|---|---|---|---|---|---|
| 5356 | 4043 | 4043 | 4043 | 4043 | 4145 | 4043 |
| NR | NR | 4043 | 4145 | 4145 | 4145 | |
| 5356 | 5356 | 5356 | 5356 | 5356 | | |
| 5356 | 5356 | 5356 | 4043 5356 | | | |
| 5356 | 5356 | 5554 | | | | |
| 5356 | 5356 | | | | | |
| 5356 | | | | | | |

* 5556 is recommended for welding 5456 to itself.

Notes:

1. The filler alloy shown is the best choice for most structural applications. Where two filler alloys are shown, either is acceptable.

2. Whenever 4043 is shown, 4047 is an acceptable alternate.

3. Whenever 5356 is shown, 5183 or 5556 are acceptable alternates.

4. Al-Mg alloys containing more than 3% Mg should not be used in applications where long-term exposures above 150° F are encountered.

5. There are applications where specific requirements make the selection of filler metal alloys other than those shown necessary.

# Filler Metal Selector Guide for Welding ASTM Steels

| ASTM No. | Grade | Product | Type of Metal | Recommended Filler Metals (AWS) | | | |
|---|---|---|---|---|---|---|---|
| | | | | SMAW | GMAW/GTAW | FCAW | |
| A3 | 1, 2 | Bars | Steel | 6012, 6013, 7014, 7024 | 70S-3, 70S-6 | 71T-1, 70T-1, 70C-3C, 70C-6M | |
| A27 | All | Castings | Steel | 7018 | 70S-3, 70S-6 | 70T-1, 71T-1, 70T-4, 70T-7, 71T-8, 70C-3C, 70C-6M | |
| A36 | | Structural | Steel | 6012, 6013, 7014, 7024, 7018 | 70S-3, 70S-6 | 71T-1, 70T-1, 70T-4, 70T-7, 70C-3C, 70C-6M | |
| A53 | A & B | Pipe | Steel | 6010, 6011 | 80S-D2, 70S-6 | 70T-1, 71T-1, 70C-3C, 70C-6M | |
| A82 | | Reinforcing | Steel | 7018, 7018-1 | 70S-3, 70S-6 | 70T-5, 70T-1, 70T-4, 71T-8, 71T-11, 70T-7, 71T-GS, 70C-3C, 70C-6M | |
| A105 | | Pipe | Steel | Same as A53 | | | |
| A106 | A & B | Pipe | Steel | Same as A53 | 80S-D2, 70S-6 | | |
| | C | Pipe | Steel | | | | |
| A109 | | Strip | Steel | 6012, 6013, 7024 | 70S-3, 70S-6 | 70T-1, 70C-3C, 70C-6M | |
| A123 | | Sheet, strip | Steel | 7018, 7018-1 | 70S-6 | 71T-11, 71T-GS, 70T-1, 71T-1, 71T-8, 70C-3C, 70C-6M | |
| A131 | | Structural | Steel | Same as A36 | | | |
| A134 | | Pipe | Steel | Same as A53 | | | |
| A135 | A & B | Pipe | Steel | Same as A53 | | | |
| A139 | All | Pipe | Steel | Same as A53 | | | |
| A148 | 80-40, 80-50 | Castings | Low alloy | 8018-C3 | 80S-D2 | 71T-1, 70T-1, 70C-3C, 70C-6M | |
| | 90-60 | Castings | Low alloy | 9018-M | | 110T5-K4 | |
| | 105-85 | Castings | Low alloy | 11018-M | | 110T5-K4 | |
| | 120-95 | Castings | Low alloy | 12018-M | | | |
| A161 | | Tubes | Steel | 6010, 6011 | 70S-6, 80S-D2 | 70T-1, 71T-1, 70C-3C, 70C-6M | |

# Filler Metal Selector Guide for Welding ASTM Steels

| ASTM No. | Grade | Product | Type of Metal | Recommended Filler Metals (AWS) | | |
|---|---|---|---|---|---|---|
| | | | | SMAW | GMAW/GTAW | FCAW |
| A167 | 304L | Sheet, strip | Stainless | 308L | 308L | 308LT-1 |
| | 309S, 309 | Sheet, strip | Stainless | 309 | 309 | 309LT-1 |
| | 310S, 310 | Sheet, strip | Stainless | 310 | | |
| | 316 | Sheet, strip | Stainless | 316 | 316L | 316LT-1 |
| | 316L, 317L | Sheet, strip | Stainless | 316L | 316L | 316LT-1 |
| | 317 | Sheet, strip | Stainless | 317L | | |
| | 347, 348 | Sheet, strip | Stainless | 347 | | |
| | XM-15 | Sheet, strip | Stainless | 310 | | |
| A176 | 429, 430 | Sheet, strip | Stainless | 308 | 309 | 309LT-1 |
| | 442, 446 | Sheet, strip | Stainless | 309 | | |
| A177 | | Sheet, strip | Stainless | 308 | 308L | 308LT-1 |
| A178 | A | Tubes | Steel | 7018 | 80S-D2 | 71T-1, 70T-1, 71T-8 |
| | C | Tubes | Steel | Same as A53 | | |
| A179 | | Tubes | Steel | Same as A53 | | |
| A181 | 60 | Pipe, fittings | Steel | Same as A53 | 80S-D2 | 71T-8 |
| | 70 | Pipe, fittings | Steel | 7018 | | |
| A182 | F1 | Pipe, fittings | C/Mo | 7018-A1 | 80S-D2 | 110T5-K4 |
| | F2, F11, F12 | Pipe, fittings | Cr/Mo | 8018-B2 | | 8018-B2 |
| | F5, F5a, F21, F22 | Pipe, fittings | Cr/Mo | 9018-B3 | | |
| | F304, F304H | Pipe, fittings | Stainless | 308 | 308L | 308LT-1 |
| | F304L | Pipe, fittings | Stainless | 308L | 308L | 308LT-1 |
| | F310 | Pipe, fittings | Stainless | 310 | | |
| | F316L | Pipe, fittings | Stainless | 316L | 316L | 316LT-1 |
| | F347H, F348, F348H | Pipe, fittings | Stainless | 347 | | |
| | F10 | Pipe, fittings | Stainless | 310 | | |
| A184 | 40 | Reinforcing | Steel | Same as A82 | | 70T-5, 70C-3C, 70C-6M, 110T5-K4 |
| | 50, 60 | Reinforcing | Low Alloy | 9018-M | | |

# Filler Metal Selector Guide for Welding ASTM Steels

| ASTM No. | Grade | Product | Type of Metal | SMAW | GMAW/GTAW | FCAW |
|---|---|---|---|---|---|---|
| | | | | | **Recommended Filler Metals (AWS)** | |
| A185 | | Reinforcing | Low alloy | 7018 | | 71T-8 |
| A192 | | Tubes | Steel | 7018 | 80S-D2, 70S-6 | 70T-1, 71T-1, 71T-8, 70C-3C, 70C-6M |
| A199 | T3b, T4, T22 | Tubes | Cr/Mo | 9018-B3 | | |
| | T11 | Tubes | Cr/Mo | 8018-B2 | | |
| A200 | | Tubes | Cr/Mo | Same as A199 | | |
| A202 | A & B | Pressure vessel | Low alloy | 9018-M | | 110T5-K4 |
| A203 | All | Pressure vessel | Nickel steel | 8018-C3 | | 81T1-Ni2, 81T1-Ni1 |
| A204 | A & B | Pressure vessel | C/Mo | 7018-A1 | 80S-D2 | 110T5-K4 |
| | C | Pressure vessel | Low alloy | 10018-M | | |
| A209 | | Tubes | Steel | 7018 | 80S-D2, 70S-6 | 70T-1, 71T-1, 71T-8, 70C-3C, 70C-6M |
| A210 | A-1 | Tubes | Steel | Same as A161 | 80S-D2, 70S-6 | 70T-1, 71T-1, 70C-3C, 70C-6M |
| | C | Tubes | Steel | 7018 | | 71T-8 |
| A211 | | Pipe | Steel | Same as A53 | | |
| A213 | T2, T11, T12, T17 | Tubes | Cr/Mo | 8018-B2 | | |
| | T3b, T22 | Tubes | Cr/Mo | 9018-B3 | | |
| | TP304, TP304H | Tubes | Stainless | 308 | 308L | 308LT-1 |
| | TP304L | Tubes | Stainless | 308L | 308L | 308LT-1 |
| | TP310 | Tubes | Stainless | 310 | | |
| | TP316, TP316H | Tubes | Stainless | 316 | 316L | 316LT-1 |
| | TP316L | Tubes | Stainless | 316L | 316L | 316LT-1 |
| | TP347, TP347H, | Tubes | Stainless | 347 | | |
| | TP348, TP348H | Tubes | Stainless | | | |
| A214 | | Tubes | Steel | Same as A161 | | |

# Filler Metal Selector Guide for Welding ASTM Steels

| ASTM No. | Grade | Product | Type of Metal | Recommended Filler Metals (AWS) | | |
|---|---|---|---|---|---|---|
| | | | | SMAW | GMAW/GTAW | FCAW |
| A216 | WCA | Castings | Steel | 6013, 7014, 7024, 7018 | 70S-3, 70S-6 | 71T-1, 70T-1, 70T-4, 70T-7, 70C-3C, 70C-6M |
| | WCB, WCC | Castings | Steel | 7024, 7018 | 70S-3, 70S-6, 80S-D2 | 71T-1, 70T-1, 70T-4, 70T-7, 71T-8, 70C-3C, 70C-6M |
| A217 | WC1 | Castings | Cr/Mo | 7024, 7018 | 70S-3, 70S-6, 80S-D2 | 71T-1, 70T-1, 70T-4, 70T-7, 71T-8, 70C-3C, 70C-6M |
| | WC4, WC5, WC6 WC9 | Castings Castings | Cr/Mo Cr/Mo | 8018-B2 9018-B3 | 80S-D2 | |
| A225 | C | Pressure vessel | Low alloy | 11018-M, 12018-M | | 110T5-K4 |
| | D | Pressure vessel | Low alloy | 8018-C3 | 80S-D2 | 81T1-Ni2, 81T1-Ni1 |
| A226 | | Tubes | Steel | Same as A161 | | |
| A234 | WPA, WPB, WPC | Fittings | Steel | Same as A53 | | |
| | WP1 | Fittings | Cr/Mo | 8018-B2 | 80S-D2 | |
| | WP11, WP12 | Fittings | Cr/Mo | 8018-B2 | | |
| | WP22 | Fittings | Cr/Mo | 9018-B3 | | |
| A236 | C, D, E, F, G | Forgings | Low alloy | 9018-M | | |
| | H | Forgings | Low alloy | 12018-M | | 110T5-K4 |
| A240 | 302, 304, 304H | Pressure vessel | Stainless | 308 | 308L | 308LT-1 |
| | 305 | Pressure vessel | Stainless | 308L | 308L | 308LT-1 |
| | 304L | Pressure vessel | Stainless | 309 | 309 | 309LT-1 |
| | 309S | Pressure vessel | Stainless | 310 | | |
| | 310S | Pressure vessel | Stainless | 316 | 316L | 316LT-1 |
| | 316H | Pressure vessel | Stainless | 316L | 316L | 316LT-1 |
| | 316L, 317L | Pressure vessel | Stainless | 317L | | |
| | 317 | Pressure vessel | Stainless | 347 | | |
| | 347, 347H | Pressure vessel | Stainless | 347 | | |
| | 348, 348H | Pressure vessel | Stainless | 310 | 310 | |

# Filler Metal Selector Guide for Welding ASTM Steels

| ASTM No. | Grade | Product | Type of Metal | Recommended Filler Metals (AWS) | | |
|---|---|---|---|---|---|---|
| | | | | SMAW | GMAW/GTAW | FCAW |
| A242 | Types 1 & 2 | Structural | Steel | 7018 | 70S-3, 70S-6 | 70T-1, 71T-1, 71T-8, 70C-3C, 70C-6M |
| A250 | | Tubes | Mo | 7018-A1 | 80S-D2 | |
| A252 | 1, 2 | Pipe | Steel | Same as A53 | 80S-D2 | |
| | 3 | Pipe | Steel | | | |
| A266 | 1, 2, 3, 4 | Forgings | Steel | 7018 | 70S-3, 70S-6 | 71T-1, 70T-1, 70T-4, 70T-7, 71T-8, 70C-3C, 70C-6M |
| A268 | TP329 | Tubes | Stainless | 309 | 309 | 309LT-1 |
| A269 | TP304 | Tubes | Stainless | 308 | 308L | 308LT-1 |
| | TP304L | Tubes | Stainless | 308L | 308L | 308LT-1 |
| | TP316 | Tubes | Stainless | 316 | 316L | 316LT-1 |
| | TP316L | Tubes | Stainless | 316L | 316L | 316LT-1 |
| | TP317 | Tubes | Stainless | 317L | | |
| | TP321, TP347 | Tubes | Stainless | 347 | | |
| A270 | | Tubes | Stainless | 308 | 308L | 308LT-1 |
| A271 | TP304 | Tubes | Stainless | 308 | 308L | 308LT-1 |
| | TP304H | Tubes | Stainless | 308 | 308L | 308LT-1 |
| | TP321 | Tubes | Stainless | 347 | | |
| | TP321H | Tubes | Stainless | 347 | | |
| | TP347 | Tubes | Stainless | 347 | | |
| | TP347H | Tubes | Stainless | 347 | | |
| A273 | C1010 thru C1020 | Forgings | Steel | 7018 | 70S-3, 70S-6 | 70T-1, 71T-1, 70T-4, 71T-8, 70C-3C, 70C-6M |

# Filler Metal Selector Guide for Welding ASTM Steels

| ASTM No. | Grade | Product | Type of Metal | SMAW | GMAW/GTAW | FCAW |
|---|---|---|---|---|---|---|
| | | | | | Recommended Filler Metals (AWS) | |
| A276 | 302, 304, 305, 302B | Bars | Stainless | 308 | 308 | 308LT-1 |
| | 304L | Bars | Stainless | 308L | 308 | 308LT-1 |
| | 309, 309S | Bars | Stainless | 309 | 309 | 309LT-1 |
| | 310, 310S | Bars | Stainless | 310 | | |
| | 316 | Bars | Stainless | 316 | 316L | 316LT-1 |
| | 316L | Bars | Stainless | 316L | 316L | 316LT-1 |
| | 317 | Bars | Stainless | 317L | | |
| | 321, 347, 348 | Bars | Stainless | 347 | | |
| | TP446 | Bars | Stainless | 309, 310 | | |
| A283 | A, B, C, D | Structural | Steel | Same as A36 | | |
| A284 | C, D | Structural | Steel | Same as A36 | | |
| A285 | A, B, C | Pressure vessel | Steel | 7018 | 70S-3, 70S-6, 80S-D2 | 71T-1, 70T-1, 71T-8, 70C-3C, 70C-6M |
| A288 | 1 | Forgings | Steel | 7018 | 70S-3, 70S-6 | 71T-1, 70T-1, 70T-4, 70T-7, 71T-8, 70C-3C, 70C-6M |
| | 2 | Forgings | Low alloy | 9018-M | | 110T5-K4 |
| | 3 | Forgings | Low alloy | 11018-M | | |
| A289 | A & B | Forgings | Stainless | 308 | 308L | 308LT-1 |
| A297 | HF | Castings | Stainless | 308, 308L | | 308LT-1 |
| | HH | Castings | Stainless | 309 | 308L | 308LT-1 |
| | HI, HK | Castings | Stainless | 310 | 309 | 309LT-1 |
| | HE | Castings | Stainless | 312 | | |
| A299 | | Pressure vessel | Low alloy | 9018-M | | |
| A302 | A, B, C, D | Pressure vessel | Low alloy | 9018-M | | |

# Filler Metal Selector Guide for Welding ASTM Steels

| ASTM No. | Grade | Product | Type of Metal | SMAW | GMAW/GTAW | FCAW |
|---|---|---|---|---|---|---|
| | | | | | Recommended Filler Metals (AWS) | |
| A312 | TP304, TP304H | Pipe | Stainless | 308 | 308L | 308LT-1 |
| | TP304L | Pipe | Stainless | 308L | 308L | 308LT-1 |
| | TP309 | Pipe | Stainless | 309 | 309 | 309LT-1 |
| | TP310 | Pipe | Stainless | 310 | | |
| | TP316, TP316H | Pipe | Stainless | 316 | 316L | 316LT-1 |
| | TP316L | Pipe | Stainless | 316L | 316L | 316LT-1 |
| | TP317 | Pipe | Stainless | 317L | | |
| | TP321, TP321H, TP347, TP347H, TP348, TP348H | Pipe | Stainless | 347 | | |
| A328 | | Piling | Steel | 7018 | 70S-3, 70S-6 | 71T-1, 70T-1, 70T-4, 70T-7, 71T-8, 70C-3C, 70C-6M |
| A333 | 1 & 6 | Pipe | Low alloy | 8018-C3 | | 81T1-Ni2, 81T1-Ni1 |
| | 3, 4, 7, 9 | Pipe | Low alloy | 8018-C2 | | |
| A334 | 1 & 6 | Tubes | Low alloy | 8018-C3 | | 81T1-Ni2, 81T1-Ni1 |
| | 3, 7, 9 | Tubes | Low alloy | 8018-C2 | | |
| A335 | P1, P15 | Pipe | C/Mo | 7018-A1 | 80S-D2 | |
| | P2, P11 P12 | Pipe | Cr/Mo | 8018-B2 | | |
| | P22 | Pipe | Cr/Mo | 9018-B3 | | |
| A336 | F1 | Pressure vessel | Low alloy | 7018-A1 | | |
| | F22, F22a | Pressure vessel | Cr/Mo | 9018-B3 | | |
| | F30 | Pressure vessel | Cr/Mo | 8018-B2 | | |
| | F31 | Pressure vessel | Nickel steel | 8018-C2 | | |
| A336 | F8, F82, F84 | Pressure vessel | Stainless | 308 | 308L | 308LT-1 |
| | F8M | Pressure vessel | Stainless | 316 | 316L | 316LT-1 |
| | FM-10, FM-25 | Pressure vessel | Stainless | 310 | | |

# Filler Metal Selector Guide for Welding ASTM Steels

| ASTM No. | Grade | Product | Type of Metal | SMAW | GMAW/GTAW | FCAW |
|---|---|---|---|---|---|---|
| | | | | | Recommended Filler Metals (AWS) | |
| A350 | LF1, LF2 | Fittings | Nickel steel | 8018-C3 | | 81T1-Ni2, 81T1-Ni1 |
| | LF3, LF4 | Fittings | Nickel steel | 8018-C2 | | |
| A351 | CF8, CF8A, CF8C | Castings | Stainless | 308 | 308L | 308LT-1 |
| | CF3, CF3A | Castings | Stainless | 308L | 308L | 308LT-1 |
| | CF8M, CF10MC, CF3M, CF3MA | Castings | Stainless | 316L | 316L | 316LT-1 |
| | CH8, CH10, CH20 CK20, HK30, HK40 | Castings | Stainless | 309 | 309 | 309LT-1 |
| | | Castings | Stainless | 310 | | |
| A352 | LC2 | Castings | Nickel steel | 8018-C1 | | 81T1-Ni2 |
| | LC3 | Castings | Nickel steel | 8018-C2 | | |
| A356 | 1 | Castings | Steel | Same as A27 | | |
| | 2 | Castings | C/Mo | 7018-A1 | 80S-D2 | |
| | 5, 6, 8 | Castings | Cr/Mo | 8018-B2 | | |
| | 10 | Castings | Cr/Mo | 9018-B3 | | |
| A358 | 304 | Pipe | Stainless | 308 | 308L | 308LT-1 |
| | 309 | Pipe | Stainless | 309 | 309 | 309LT-1 |
| | 310 | Pipe | Stainless | 310 | | |
| | 316 | Pipe | Stainless | 316 | 316L | 316LT-1 |
| | 321, 347, 348 | Pipe | Stainless | 347 | | |
| A361 | | Sheet | Steel | 7018 | 70S-6 | 71T-11, 71T-GS, 70T-1, 71T-8, 71T-1 |
| A369 | FP1 | Pipe | Low alloy | 7018-A1 | 80S-D2 | |
| | FP2, FP11, FP12 | Pipe | Cr/Mo | 8018-B2 | | |
| | FP22, FP3B | Pipe | Cr/Mo | 9018-B3 | | |
| A369 | FPA, FPB | Pipe | Low alloy | 7018 | 70S-3, 70S-6 | 70T-1, 71T-1, 70T-4, 70T-7, 71T-8, 70C-3C, 70C-6M |

# Filler Metal Selector Guide for Welding ASTM Steels

| ASTM No. | Grade | Product | Type of Metal | SMAW | GMAW/GTAW | FCAW |
|---|---|---|---|---|---|---|
| | | | | | Recommended Filler Metals (AWS) | |
| A372 | I | Forgings | Steel | 7018 | 70S-3, 70S-6 | 70T-1, 71T-1, 70T-4, 70T-7, 71T-8, 70C-3C, 70C-6M, 110T5-K4 |
| | II, III | Forgings | Low alloy | 9018-M | | |
| | IV | Forgings | Low alloy | 11018-M | | 110T5-K4 |
| | V | Forgings | Alloy steel | 12018-M | | |
| | VI | Forgings | Alloy steel | 10018-D2 | | 110T5-K4 |
| A376 | TP304, TP304H, TP304N | Pipe | Stainless | 308 | 308L | 308LT-1 |
| | TP316, TP316H, TP316N | Pipe | Stainless | 316 | 316L | 316LT-1 |
| | TP321, TP321H, TP347, TP347H, TP348 | Pipe | Stainless | 347 | | |
| A381 | Y35 thru Y50, Y52, Y56 | Pipe | Steel | Same as A53 7010, 7018 | 80S-D2 | 71T8-K6, 71T-8 |
| | Y60, Y65 | Pipe | Low alloy | 9018-M | | |
| A387 | A, B, C | Pressure vessel | Cr/Mo | 8018-B2 | | |
| | D, E | Pressure vessel | Cr/Mo | 9018-B3 | | |
| A389 | C23 | Castings | Cr/Mo | 8018-B2 | | |
| A403 | WP304, WP304H | Fittings | Stainless | 308 | 308L | 308LT-1 |
| | WP304L | Fittings | Stainless | 308L | 308L | 308LT-1 |
| | WP309 | Fittings | Stainless | 309 | 309 | 309LT-1 |
| | WP310 | Fittings | Stainless | 310 | | |
| | WP316, WP316H | Fittings | Stainless | 316 | 316L | 316LT-1 |
| | WP317 | Fittings | Stainless | 317L | | |
| | WP321, WP321H, WP347H, WP348 | Fittings | Stainless | 347 | | |
| A405 | P24 | Pipe | Cr/Mo | 9018-B3 | | |

# Filler Metal Selector Guide for Welding ASTM Steels

| ASTM No. | Grade | Product | Type of Metal | SMAW | GMAW/GTAW | FCAW |
|---|---|---|---|---|---|---|
| | | | | | **Recommended Filler Metals (AWS)** | |
| A409 | TP304, TP304L | Pipe | Stainless | 308 | 308L | 308LT-1 |
| | TP309 | Pipe | Stainless | 309 | 309 | 309LT-1 |
| | TP310 | Pipe | Stainless | 310 | | |
| | TP316, TP316L | Pipe | Stainless | 316 | 316L | 316LT-1 |
| | TP317 | Pipe | Stainless | 317L | | |
| | TP321, TP347, TP348 | Pipe | Stainless | 347 | | |
| A412 | 201, 202 | Sheet, strip | Stainless | 308 | 308L | 308LT-1 |
| A413 | PC, BBB | Chain | Steel | 7018 | 70S-3 | 70T-1, 71T-1, 70T-4, 70T-7, 71T-8, 70C-3C, 70C-6M |
| A414 | A, B, C, D, E, F, G | Sheet | Steel | 6012, 6013, 7014, 7024-1 | 70S-3, 70S-6 | 70T-1, 71T-1, 70T-4,70T-7, 70C-3C, 70C-6M |
| A420 | WPL6 | Fittings | Steel | 8018-C3 | | 81T1-Ni2, 81T1-Ni1 |
| | WPL9 | Fittings | Nickel steel | 8018-C1 | | 81T1-Ni2 |
| | WPL3 | Fittings | Nickel steel | 8018-C2 | | |
| A423 | 1 | Tubes | Cr/Mo | 8018-B2 | | |
| | 2 | Tubes | Nickel steel | 8018-C3 | | 81T1-Ni2, 81T1-Ni1 |
| A426 | CP1, CP15 | Pipe | Cr/Mo | 7018-A1 | 80S-D2 | |
| | CP2, CP11, CP12 | Pipe | Cr/Mo | 8018-B2 | | |
| | CP21, CP22 | Pipe | Cr/Mo | 9018-B3 | | |
| A430 | FP304, FP304H, FP304N | Pipe | Stainless | 308 | 308L | 308LT-1 |
| | FP316, FP316H, FP316N | Pipe | Stainless | 316 | 316L | 316LT-1 |
| | FP321, FP321H, FP347, FP347H | Pipe | Stainless | 347 | | |
| A441 | | Structural | Steel | Same as A36 | | |
| A442 | 55, 60 | Pressure vessel | Nickel steel | 8018-C3 | | 81T1-Ni2, 81T1-Ni1 |
| A447 | | Castings | Stainless | 309 | 309 | 309LT-1 |
| A451 | CPF8, CPF8C | Pipe | Stainless | 308 | 308L | 308LT-1 |
| | CPH8, CPH20 | Pipe | Stainless | 309 | 309 | 309LT-1 |
| | CPK20 | Pipe | Stainless | 310 | | |

# Filler Metal Selector Guide for Welding ASTM Steels

| ASTM No. | Grade | Product | Type of Metal | Recommended Filler Metals (AWS) | | |
|---|---|---|---|---|---|---|
| | | | | SMAW | GMAW/GTAW | FCAW |
| A452 | TP304H | Pipe | Stainless | 308 | 308L | 308LT-1 |
| | TP316H | Pipe | Stainless | 316 | 316L | 316LT-1 |
| | TP347H | Pipe | Stainless | 347 | | |
| A455 | | Pressure vessel | Low alloy | 9018-M | | |
| A457 | 761 | Sheet, strip | Stainless | 347 | | |
| A469 | 1, 2 | Forgings | Nickel steel | 8018-C2 | | |
| A470 | 1, 2 | Forgings | Nickel steel | 8018-C2 | | |
| A479 | 302, 304, 304H | Bars | Stainless | 308 | 308L | 308LT-1 |
| | 304L | Bars | Stainless | 308L | 308L | 308LT-1 |
| | 310, 310S | Bars | Stainless | 310 | | |
| | 316, 316H | Bars | Stainless | 316 | 316L | 316LT-1 |
| | 316L | Bars | Stainless | 316L | 316L | 316LT-1 |
| | 321, 321H, 347, 347H, 348, 348H | Bars | Stainless | 347 | | |
| A486 | 70 | Castings | Steel | 7014, 7024, 7018 | 70S-3, 70S-6 | 70T-1, 71T-1, 70T-4, 70T-7, 70C-3C, 70C-6M, 110T5-K4 |
| | 90 | Castings | Low alloy | 9018-M | | |
| | 120 | Castings | Alloy steel | 12018-M | | |
| A487 | 1N, 2N, 4N, 8N, 9N, 1Q, 2Q 3Q, 4Q, 5Q, 4QA, 7Q, | Castings | Low alloy | 9018-M | | 110T5-K4 |
| | | Castings | Alloy steel | 12018-M | | |
| A496 | | Reinforcing | Low alloy | 9018-M | | |
| A497 | | Reinforcing | Low alloy | 9018-M | | |

# Filler Metal Selector Guide for Welding ASTM Steels

| ASTM No. | Grade | Product | Type of Metal | Recommended Filler Metals (AWS) | | |
|---|---|---|---|---|---|---|
| | | | | SMAW | GMAW/GTAW | FCAW |
| A500 | A, B, C | Tubes | Steel | Same as A36 | | |
| A501 | | Tubes | Steel | Same as A161 | | |
| A508 | | Forgings | Steel | 7018 | 70S-3, 70S-6 | 70T1, 71T-1, 70T-4, 70T-7, 71T-8, 70C-3C, 70C-6M |
| | 1, 1a | Forgings | Low alloy | 9018-M | | 110T5-K4 |
| | 2, 3 | Forgings | Low alloy | 11018-M | | 110T5-K4 |
| | 4, 5 | Forgings | Low alloy | 12018-M | | |
| | 5a, 4a | | | | | |
| A511 | MT302, MT304, | Tubes | Stainless | 308 | 308L | 308LT-1 |
| | MT305 | Tubes | Stainless | 308L | 308L | 308LT-1 |
| | MT304L | Tubes | Stainless | 309 | 309 | 309LT-1 |
| | MT309, MT309S | Tubes | Stainless | 310 | 310 | |
| | MT310, MT310S | Tubes | Stainless | 316 | 316L | 316LT-1 |
| | MT316 | Tubes | Stainless | 316L | 316L | 316LT-1 |
| | MT316L | Tubes | Stainless | 317L | | |
| | MT317 | Tubes | Stainless | 347 | | |
| | MT321, MT347 | | | | | |
| A512 | MT1010 thru MT1020 | Tubes | Steel | Same as A216 | | |
| A513 | 1008 thru 1022 | Tubes | Steel | Same as A161 | | |
| A514 | | Plates | Low alloy | 11018-M, 12018-M | | 110T5-K4 |
| A515 | | Pressure vessel | Steel | 7018 | 70S-3 | 70T-1, 71T-1, 70T-4, 70T-7, 71T-8, 70C-3C, 70C-6M |
| A516 | | Pressure vessel | Steel | 7018 | 70S-3 | 81T1-Ni2, 70T-1, 71T-1, 70T-4, 71T-8, 70T-7, 70C-3C, 70C-6M |
| A517 | | Pressure vessel | Low alloy | 11018-M | | 110T5-K4 |
| A519 | 1008 thru 4130 | Tubes | Steel | Same as A161 | | |

# Filler Metal Selector Guide for Welding ASTM Steels

| ASTM No. | Grade | Product | Type of Metal | Recommended Filler Metals (AWS) | | |
|---|---|---|---|---|---|---|
| | | | | SMAW | GMAW/GTAW | FCAW |
| A521 | CA, CC, CC1 | Forgings | Steel | 7018 | 70S-3, 70S-6 | 70T-1, 71T-1, 70T-4, 70T-7, 71T-8, 70C-3C, 70C-6M |
| | AA, AB, CE, CF, AC, AD, CF1, CG, AE | Forgings | Low alloy | 9018-M | | 110T5-K4 |
| | | Forgings | Low alloy | 11018-M | | 110T5-K4 |
| A523 | | Pipe | Steel | Same as A53 | | |
| A524 | | Pipe | Steel | Same as A53 | | |
| A526 | | Sheet | Galvanized | 7018 | 70S-6 | 71T-11, 71T-GS |
| A527 | | Sheet | Galvanized | 7018 | 70S-6 | 71T-11, 71T-GS |
| A528 | | Sheet | Galvanized | 7018 | 70S-6 | 71T-11, 71T-GS |
| A529 | | Structural | Steel | Same as A36 | | |
| A533 | A1, B1, C1, D1 | Pressure vessel | Low alloy | 9018-M | | 110T5-K4 |
| | A2, B2, C2, D2, A3, B3, C3, D3 | Pressure vessel | Low alloy | 10018-M | | 110T5-K4 |
| A537 | 1 | Pressure vessel | Steel | 7018 | 70S-3 | 70T-1, 71T-1, 71T-8 |
| | 2 | Pressure vessel | Nickel steel | 8018-C3 | | 81T1-Ni2, 81T1-Ni1 |
| A539 | | Tubes | Steel | Same as A161 | | |
| A541 | 1, 1a | Forgings | Steel | 7018 | 70S-3, 70S-6 | 70T-1, 71T-1, 70T-4, 70T-7, 71T-8, 70C-3C, 70C-6M |
| | 2, 3, 4, 5, 6, 6A, 7, 7A, 8, 8A | Forgings | Cr/Mo, Low alloy | 8018-B2, 12018-M | | |
| A542 | 1, 2 | Pressure vessel | Cr/Mo | 9018-B3 | | |
| A543 | A, B | Pressure vessel | Low alloy | 12018-M | | |

# Filler Metal Selector Guide for Welding ASTM Steels

| ASTM No. | Grade | Product | Type of Metal | SMAW | GMAW/GTAW | FCAW |
|---|---|---|---|---|---|---|
| | | | | | | **Recommended Filler Metals (AWS)** |
| A554 | MT301, MT302, MT304, MT305 | Tubes | Stainless | 308 | 308L | 308LT-1 |
| | MT304L | Tubes | Stainless | 308L | 308L | 308LT-1 |
| | MT309, MT309S | Tubes | Stainless | 309 | 309 | 309LT-1 |
| | MT310, MT310S | Tubes | Stainless | 310 | | |
| | MT316 | Tubes | Stainless | 316 | 316L | 316LT-1 |
| | MT316L | Tubes | Stainless | 316L | 316L | 316LT-1 |
| | MT317 | Tubes | Stainless | 317L | | |
| | MT321, MT347 | Tubes | Stainless | 347 | | |
| A556 | A2, B2 | Tubes | Stainless | Same as A161 | | |
| | C2 | Tubes | Steel | 7018 | 70S-6, 80S-D2 | 71T-1, 70C-3C, 70C-6M, 70T-1 |
| A557 | | Tubes | Steel | Same as A556 | | |
| A562 | | Pressure vessel | Steel | 7018 | 70S-3 | 71T-1, 70T-1, 71T-8, 71T-11, 70C-3C, 70C-6M |
| A569 | | Sheet, strip | Steel | 6012, 6022, 6013, 7014 | 70S-3, 70S-6 | 71T-11, 71T-GS, 71T-1, 70T-1, 70C-3C, 70C-6M |
| A570 | 30, 36, 40, 45 | Sheet, strip | Steel | Any E60 or E70 electrode | 70S-3, 70S-6 | 70T-1, 71T-1, 71T-8, 70C-3C, 70C-6M |
| | 50 | Sheet, strip | Steel | 7018, 7024 | 70S-3, 70S-6 | 70T-4, 70T-7, 70T-1, 71T-1, 71T-8, 70C-3C, 70C-6M |
| A572 | 42 thru 55 | Structural | Steel | Same as A36 | | |
| | 60 thru 65 | Structural | Low alloy | 8018-C2 | | |
| A573 | | Structural | Steel | Same as A36 | | |
| A587 | | Pipe | Steel | Same as A53 | | |
| A588 | | Structural | Steel | 7018 | 70S-3, 70S-6 | 71T-8 |
| A589 | | Pipe | Steel | Same as A53 | | 7118-K6 |
| A591 | | Sheet | Galvanized | 7018 | 70S-6 | 71T-11, 71T-GS |
| A592 | A, E, F | Pressure vessel | Low alloy | 12018-M | | |
| A595 | A, B, C | Tubes | Steel | 7018 | 70S-3, 70S-6 | 71T-1, 70T-1, 71T-8 |
| A606 | | Sheet | Low alloy | 7018 | 70S-3, 70S-6 | 71T-1, 70T-1, 70T-4, 70T-7, 71T-11, 71T-GS, 70C-3C, 70C-6M |

# Filler Metal Selector Guide for Welding ASTM Steels

| ASTM No. | Grade | Product | Type of Metal | Recommended Filler Metals (AWS) | | |
|---|---|---|---|---|---|---|
| | | | | SMAW | GMAW/GTAW | FCAW |
| A607 | 45 | Sheet | Low alloy | 6010, 6011, 6012, 6013, 7014, 7024, 7018 | 70S-3, 70S-6, 80S-D2 | 71T-1, 70T-1, 70C-3C, 70C-6M, 70T-4, 70T-7, 71T-11, 71T-GS |
| | 50 | Sheet | Low alloy | 7018 | 70S-3, 70S-6 | 71T-1, 70T-1, 70C-3C, 70C-6M, 70T-4, 70T-7, 71T-8, 71T-11, 71T-GS |
| | 60 | Sheet | Low alloy | 8018-C3 | | 81T2-Ni2, 81T1-Ni1 |
| | 70 | Sheet | Low alloy | 9018-M | | 110T5-K4 |
| A611 | A, B, C, D | Sheet | Steel | Any E60 or E70 electrode | 70S-3, 70S-6 | 71T-1, 70T-1, 70C-3C, 70C-6M, 70T-4, 70T-7, 71T-8 |
| A611 | E | Sheet | Steel | 9018-M | 80S-D2 | 110T5-K4 |
| A612 | | Pressure vessel | Steel | 9018-M | 80S-D2 | 110T5-K4 |
| A615 | 40 | Reinforcing | Steel | Same as A82 | 80S-D2 | |
| | 60 | Reinforcing | Low alloy | 9018-M | 80S-D2 | 110T5-K4 |
| | 75 | Reinforcing | Low alloy | 10018-M | 80S-D2 | 110T5-K4 |
| A616 | 50, 60 | Reinforcing | Low alloy | 9018-M | 80S-D2 | 110T5-K4 |
| A617 | 40 | Reinforcing | Steel | Same as A82 | 80S-D2 | |
| | 60 | Reinforcing | Low alloy | 9018-M | 80S-D2 | 110T5-K4 |
| A618 | 1, 2, 3 | Tubes | Steel | 7018, 7024 | 80S-D2 | 71T-8 |
| A620 | | Sheet | Steel | 7014, 7024 | 70S-3 | 71T-11, 71T-GS, 71T-1 |
| A621 | | Sheet, strip | Steel | 7018 | 70S-6 | 70T-1, 71T-1, 71T-8 |
| A632 | TP304 | Tubes | Stainless | 308 | 308L | 308LT-1 |
| | TP304L | Tubes | Stainless | 308L | 308L | 308LT-1 |
| | TP310 | Tubes | Stainless | 310 | 310 | |
| | TP316 | Tubes | Stainless | 316 | 316L | 316LT-1 |
| | TP316L | Tubes | Stainless | 316L | 316L | 316LT-1 |
| | TP317 | Tubes | Stainless | 317L | | |
| | TP321 | Tubes | Stainless | 347 | | |
| | TP347 | Tubes | Stainless | 347 | | |
| | TP348 | Tubes | Stainless | 347 | | |

# Filler Metal Selector Guide for Welding ASTM Steels

| ASTM No. | Grade | Product | Type of Metal | Recommended Filler Metals (AWS) | | | |
|---|---|---|---|---|---|---|---|
| | | | | SMAW | GMAW/GTAW | FCAW | |
| A633 | A, B, C, D | Structural | High strength, Low alloy | 7018 | 70S-3, 70S-6 | 71T-1, 70T-1, 70C-3C, 70C-6M, 71T-11, 71T-GS, 70T-4, 70T-7, 71T-8 | |
| A642 | | Sheet | Galvanized | 7018 | 70S-6 | 71T-11, 71T-GS, 71T-8 | |
| A643 | A | Castings | Steel | 7018, 7024 | 70S-3, 70S-6, 80S-D2 | 70T-1, 71T-1, 70T-3C, 70C-6M, 70T-4, 70T-7, 71T-8 | |
| | B | Castings | Steel | 10018-D2 | | 110T5-K4 | |
| | C | Castings | Steel | 9018-B3 | | | |
| A651 | TPXM8 | Tubes | Stainless | 347 | 308L | 308LT-1 | |
| | TP304 | Tubes | Stainless | 308 | 316L | 316LT-1 | |
| | TP316 | Tubes | Stainless | 316 | | | |
| A656 | 1, 2 | Structural | Low alloy | 10018-D2 | | 110T5-K4 | |
| A659 | 1015, 1016, 1017, 1018, 1020, 1023 | Sheet strip | Steel | Same as A607 | 70S-3, 70S-6, 80S-D2 | 70T-1, 71T-1, 70C-3C, 70C-6M, 70T-4, 70T-7 | |
| A660 | WCC, WCA, WCB | Pipe | Carbon steel pipe | 7018 | 70S-3, 70S-6 | 70T-1, 71T-1, 71T-8, 70C-3C, 70C-6M | |
| A662 | A, B | Pressure vessel | C-Mn | 7018 | 70S-3, 70S-6 | 70T-1, 71T-1, 71T-8, 70C-3C, 70C-6M, 70T-470T-7 | |
| A666 | TP301 | Sheet, strip | Stainless | 308 | 308L | 308LT-1 | |
| | TP316 | Sheet, strip | Stainless | 316 | 316L | 316LT-1 | |

# Filler Metal Selector Guide for Welding ASTM Steels

| ASTM No. | Grade | Product | Type of Metal | SMAW | GMAW/GTAW | FCAW |
|---|---|---|---|---|---|---|
| | | | | | *Recommended Filler Metals (AWS)* | |
| A669 | | Tubes | Alloy steel | 316L | 316L | 316LT-1 |
| A672 | B65 | Pipe | Steel | 7018 | 70S-3 | 70T-1, 71T-1, 71T-8, 70C-3C, 70C-6M |
| | D80, E55, E60 | Pipe | Steel | 8018-C3 | | 81T1-Ni2, 81T1-Ni1 |
| | H75, H80, J80, J90 | Pipe | Steel | 9018-M | | 110T5-K4 |
| | J100 | Pipe | Steel | 10018-M | | 110T5-K4 |
| | K75, K85 | Pipe | Steel | 9018-M | 80S-D2 | 110T5-K4 |
| | L65, L70 | Pipe | Steel | 7018-A1 | | 110T5-K4 |
| | L75 | Pipe | Steel | 10018-M | | 110T5-K4 |
| | M70, M75, N75 | Pipe | Steel | 9018-M | | 110T5-K4 |
| A678 | A | Structural | Carbon steel | 7018 | 70S-3, 70S-6 | 70T-1, 71T-1, 71T-8, 70C-3C, 70C-6M, 70T-4, 70T-7 |
| A678 | B | Structural | Carbon steel | 9018-M | | 110T5-K4 |
| | C | Structural | Carbon steel | 10018-M | | |
| A688 | TP304 | Tubes | Stainless steel | 308 | 308L | 308LT-1 |
| | TP304L | Tubes | Stainless steel | 308L | 308L | 308LT-1 |
| | TP316 | Tubes | Stainless steel | 316 | 316L | 316LT-1 |
| | TP316L | Tubes | Stainless steel | 316L | 316L | 316LT-1 |
| A691 | CM65, CM70 | Pipe | C & Alloy steel | 7018-A1 | 80S-D2 | 110T5-K4 |
| | CM75 | Pipe | C & Alloy steel | 10018-M | | 110T5-K4 |
| | CMSH70 | Pipe | C & Alloy steel | 7018 | | 70T-1, 71T-1, 71T-8, 70C-3C, 70C-6M |
| | CMS75 | Pipe | C & Alloy steel | 9018-M | 70S-3 | 110T5-K4 |
| | CMSH80 | Pipe | C & Alloy steel | 8018-C3 | | 81T1-Ni2, 81T1-Ni1 |
| | 1/2CR | Pipe | C & Alloy steel | 8018-B2 | | |
| | 1CR, 1-1/4CR | Pipe | C & Alloy steel | 8018-B2 | | |
| | 2-1/4CR | Pipe | C & Alloy steel | 9018-B3 | | |

# Filler Metal Selector Guide for Welding ASTM Steels

| ASTM No. | Grade | Product | Type of Metal | Recommended Filler Metals (AWS) | | |
|---|---|---|---|---|---|---|
| | | | | SMAW | GMAW/GTAW | FCAW |
| A692 | | Tubes | Cr/Mo | 7018-A1 | 80S-D2 | 110T5-K4 |
| A694 | F42, F46, R48 | Fittings | C & Alloy steel | 7018 | 70S-3, 70S-6 | 70T-1, 71T-1, 71T-8, 70C-3C, 70C-6M, 70T-4, 70T-7 |
| | F56, F50, F52 | Fittings | C & Alloy steel | 7018 | 70S-3, 70S-6 | 70T-1, 71T-1, 71T-8, 70C-3C, 70C-6M, 70T-4, 70T-7 |
| | F60, F65 | Fittings | C & Alloy steel | 8018-C3 | 80S-D2 | 81T1-Ni2, 81T1-Ni1 |
| A696 | B, C | Bars | Steel | 7018 | 70S-3, 70S-6 | 70T-1, 71T-1, 71T-8, 70C-3C, 70C-6M, 70T-4, 70T-7 |
| A699 | 1, 2, 3, 4 | Plates, bars | Low alloy | 10018-D2 | | 110T5-K4 |
| A704 | 40 | Reinforcing | Steel | 7018 | 70S-3, 70S-6 | 70T-1, 71T-1, 70C-3C, 70C-6M, 70T-4, 70T-7, 71T-8, 71T-11, 71T-GS |
| | 60 | Reinforcing | Steel | 9018-M | 80S-D2 | 110T5-K4 |
| A706 | | Reinforcing | Low alloy | 8018-C3 | 80S-D2 | 81T1-Ni2, 81T1-Ni1 |
| A707 | L1, L2, L3 | Flanges | C & Alloy steel | 7018 | 70S-3, 70S-6 | 70T-1, 71T-1, 70C-3C, 70C-6M, 70T-4, 70T-7, 71T-8 |
| | L4 | Flanges | C & Alloy steel | 8018-C1 | 80S-D2 | 81T1-Ni2 |
| | L5, L6 | Flanges | C & Alloy steel | 8018-C3 | 80S-D2 | 81T1-Ni2, 81T1-Ni1 |
| | L7, L8 | Flanges | C & Alloy steel | 8018-C2 | 80S-D2 | |
| A709 | 36 | Structural | High strength, Low alloy | 6012, 6013, 7014, 7024, 7018 | 70S-3, 70S-6 | 70T-1, 71T-1, 70C-3C, 70C-6M, 70T-4, 70T-7, 71T-8, 71T-11, 71T-GS |
| | 50, 50W | Structural | High strength, Low alloy | 7018 | 70S-3, 70S-6 | E70T-1, 71T-1, 71T-8, 70C-3C, 70C-6M, 70T-4, 70T-7, 110T5-K4 |
| | 100, 100W | Structural | High strength, Low alloy | 11018-M | | |

# Filler Metal Selector Guide for Welding ASTM Steels

| ASTM No. | Grade | Product | Type of Metal | SMAW | GMAW/GTAW | FCAW |
|---|---|---|---|---|---|---|
| A714 | I, II, III, IV | Pipe | Low alloy | 7018 | 70S-3, 70S-6 | 70T-1, 71T-1, 71T-8, 70C-3C, 70C-6M |
| | V | Pipe | Low alloy | 8018-C1 | | 81T1-Ni2 |
| | VI | Pipe | Low alloy | 8018-C3 | | 81T1-Ni2, 81T1-Ni1 |
| A715 | 50 | Sheet, strip | Steel | 6012, 6013, 7024, 7018 | 70S-3, 70S-6 | 70T-1, 71T-1, 70C-3C, 70C-6M, 70T-4, 70T-7 |
| | 60 | Sheet, strip | Steel | 7018, 7024, 7014 | 80S-D2 | 70T-1, 71T-1, 71T-8, 70C-3C, 70C-6M |
| | 70 | Sheet, strip | Steel | 7018 | 70S-3, 70S-6, 80S-D2 | 70T-1, 71T-1, 70C-3C, 70C-6M, 70T-4, 70T-7 |
| | 80 | Sheet, strip | Steel | 9018-M | 80S-D2 | 110T5-K4 |
| A724 | A | Pressure vessel | Q & T steel | 9018-M | | 110T5-K4 |
| A732 | 1A, 2A, 3A | Castings | Steel | 6012, 6013, 7024, 7014, 7018 | 70S-3, 70S-6 | 70T-1, 71T-1, 70C-3C, 70C-6M, 70T-4, 70T-7 |
| | 4A | Castings | Steel | 9018-M | | 110T5-K4 |
| | 5N, 6N | Castings | Steel | 7024, 7018 | 70S-3, 80S-D2 | 70T-1, 71T-1, 70T-4, 70T-7, 71T-8, 70C-3C, 70C-6M |
| A734 | A | Pressure vessel | Alloy & Low alloy | 8018-B2 | | |
| | B | Pressure vessel | Alloy & Low alloy | 9018-M | 80S-D2 | 110T5-K4 |
| A735 | 1, 2, 3 | Pressure vessel | Low C & Alloy steel | 9018-M | 80S-D2 | 110T5-K4 |
| | 4 | Pressure vessel | Low C & Alloy steel | 10018-D2 | | 110T5-K4 |
| A736 | 2 | Pressure vessel | Alloy | 8018-B2 | | 110T5-K4 |
| | 3 | Pressure vessel | Alloy | 9018-M | 80S-D2 | |
| | B | Pressure vessel | Low alloy | 7018 | 70S-3, 70S-6 | 70T-1, 71T-1, 70T-4, 70T-7, 71T-8, 70C-3C, 70C-6M |

# Filler Metal Selector Guide for Welding ASTM Steels

| ASTM No. | Grade | Product | Type of Metal | Recommended Filler Metals (AWS) | | |
|---|---|---|---|---|---|---|
| | | | | SMAW | GMAW/GTAW | FCAW |
| A737 | C | Pressure vessel | Low alloy | 9018-M | 80S-D2 | 110T5-K4 |
| A738 | | Pressure vessel | Alloy | 9018-M | 80S-D2 | 110T5-K4 |
| A744 | CF-8 | Castings | Stainless | 308 | 308 | |
| | CF-8M | Castings | Stainless | 316 | 316 | |
| | CF-8C | Castings | Stainless | 347 | | |
| | CF-3 | Castings | Stainless | 308L | 308L | 308LT-1 |
| | CG-8M | Castings | Stainless | 316L, 317L | 316L | 316LT-1 |
| A757 | A2Q | Castings | Alloy steel | 7018 | | 71T-8 |
| | B2N, B2Q | Castings | Alloy steel | 8018-C1 | | 81T1-Ni2 |
| | B3N, B3Q | Castings | Alloy steel | 8018-C2 | | |
| | C1Q | Castings | Alloy steel | 10018-M | | |
| | DNDQ | Castings | Alloy steel | 9018-B3 | | |
| | E1Q | Castings | Alloy steel | 11018-M | | |
| A765 | 1 | Pressure vessel | Low alloy | 7018 | | 71T-1, 70T-1, 71T-8 |
| | 2 | Pressure vessel | Low alloy | 7018-1 | | 71T-1, 70T-1, 71T-8 |
| A771 | | Tubing | Stainless | 316H | | |
| A782 | Class 1 | Pressure vessel | High strength, Mn-Cr-Mo | 9018-M | 80S-D2 | 110T5-K4 |
| | Class 2 | Pressure vessel | High Strength, Mn-Cr-Mo | 11018-M | | 110T5-K4 |
| | Class 3 | Pressure vessel | High strength, Mn-Cr-Mo | 12018-M | | |
| A808 | | Steel plate | High strength, low alloy | 7018-1 | | 71T-1, 70T-1, 71T-8 |

# Filler Metal Selector Guide for Welding ASTM Steels

| ASTM No. | Grade | Product | Type of Metal | Recommended Filler Metals (AWS) | | |
|---|---|---|---|---|---|---|
| | | | | SMAW | GMAW/GTAW | FCAW |
| A812 | 65 | Sheet | High strength, low alloy | 9018-M | 80S-D2 | 110T5-K4 |
| | 8 | Sheet | High strength, low alloy | 11018-M, 10018-M | | 110T5-K4 |
| A813 | TP304 | Pipe | Stainless | 308 | 308 | 308LT-1 |
| | TP304H | Pipe | Stainless | 308H | | |
| | TP304L | Pipe | Stainless | 308L | 308L | |
| | TP309S | Pipe | Stainless | 309 | 309 | |
| | TP310S | Pipe | Stainless | 310 | | |
| | TP316 | Pipe | Stainless | 316 | 316 | |
| | TP316H | Pipe | Stainless | 316H | | |
| | TP316L | Pipe | Stainless | 316L | 316L | 316LT-1 |
| | TP317 | Pipe | Stainless | 317L | | |
| | TP317L | Pipe | Stainless | 317L | | |
| | TP321 | Pipe | Stainless | 347 | | |
| | TP347 | Pipe | Stainless | 347 | | |
| A814 | | Pipe | Stainless | Same as A813 | | |
| A822 | | Tubing | Steel | 6010, 6011, 6013 | | |
| A826 | TP316 | Tubes | Stainless | 316H | | |
| A830 | | Plates | Steel | 7018 | 70S-3, 70S-6 | 70T-1, 71T-1, 71T-8, 70C-3C, 70C-6M |
| A841 | | Pressure vessel | Steel | 7018 | | 71T-1, 70T-1, 71T-8 |
| A851 | TP304 | Tubes | Stainless | 308, 308H | 308 | 308LT-1 |
| | TP304L | Tubes | Stainless | 308L | 308L | |
| A873 | | Sheet, strip | Steel | 9018-B3, 9018-B3L | | |

# Welding Terms & Definitions
Source: AWS

**AC or Alternating Current** — Is that kind of electricity which reverses its direction periodically. For 60 cycle current, the current goes in one direction and then in the other direction 60 times in the same second, so that the current changes its direction 120 times in one second.

**Arc Blow** — The deflection of an arc from its normal path because of magnetic forces.

**Arc Length** — The distance from the tip of the welding electrode to the adjacent surface of the weld pool.

**Arc Voltage** — The voltage across the welding arc.

**As-Welded** — Pertaining to the condition of weld metal, welded joints, and weldments after welding, but prior to any subsequent thermal, mechanical or chemical treatments.

**Automatic Welding** — welding with equipment that requires only occasional or no observation of the welding, and no manual adjustments of the equipment controls.

**Backing** — A material or device placed against the backside of the joint, or at both sides of a weld in electroslag and electrogas welding, to support and retain molten weld metal. The material may be partially fused or remain unfused during welding and may be either metal or nonmetal.

**Backstep Sequence** — A longitudinal sequence in which weld passes are made in the direction opposite to the progress of welding.

**Bare Electrode** — A filler metal electrode produced as a wire, strip, or bar with no coating or covering except one incidental to its manufacture or preservation.

**Base Material** — The material being welded, brazed, soldered, or cut.

**Butt Joint** — A joint between two members aligned approximately in the same plane.

**Concavity** — The maximum distance from the face of a concave fillet weld perpendicular to a line joining the weld toes.

**Convexity** — The maximum distance from the face of a convex fillet weld perpendicular to a line joining the weld toes.

**Covered Electrode** — A composite filler metal electrode consisting of a bare or metal cored electrode with a flux covering sufficient to provide a slag layer and/or alloying elements. The covering may contain materials providing such functions as shielding from the atmosphere, deoxidation, and arc stabilization and can serve as a source of metallic additions to the weld.

**Crater** — A depression in the weld at the termination of a weld bead.

**Depth of Fusion** — The distance that fusion extends into the base metal or previous bead from the surface melted during welding.

**DC or Direct Current** — Electric current which flows only in one direction. In welding, an arc welding process wherein the power supply at the arc is direct current.

**Fillet Weld** — A weld of approximately triangular cross section joining two surfaces approximately at right angles to each other in a lap joint, T-joint or corner joint.

**Fillet Weld Leg** — The distance from the joint root to the toe of the fillet weld.

**Flat Welding Position** — The welding position used to weld from the upper side of the joint at a point where the weld axis is approximately horizontal, and the weld face lies in an approximately horizontal plane.

**Flux** — A material applied to the workpiece(s) before or during joining or surfacing to cause interactions that remove oxides and other contaminants, improve wetting, and affect the final surface profile.

**Flux Cored Arc Welding (FCAW)** — An arc welding process that uses an arc between a continuous filler metal electrode and the weld pool. The process is used with shielding gas from a flux contained within the tubular electrode, with or without additional shielding from an externally supplied gas, and without the application of pressure.

**Gas Metal Arc Welding (GMAW)** — An arc welding process that uses an arc between a continuous filler metal electrode and the weld pool. The process is used with shielding from an externally supplied gas and without the application of pressure.

**Gas Tungsten Arc Welding (GTAW)** — An arc welding process that uses an arc between a tungsten electrode (nonconsumable) and the weld pool. The process is used with shielding gas and without the application of pressure.

**Groove Weld** — A weld in a weld groove on a workpiece surface, between workpiece edges, between workpiece surfaces, or between workpiece edges and surfaces.

**Heat-Affected Zone** — The portion of the base metal whose mechanical properties or microstructure have been altered by the heat of welding, brazing, soldering, or thermal cutting.

**Horizontal Welding Position** —
   **Fillet Weld** - The welding position in which the weld is on the upper side of an approximately horizontal surface and against an approximately vertical surface.
   **Groove Weld** — The welding position in which the weld face lies in an approximately vertical plane and the weld axis at the point of welding is approximately horizontal.

**Joint Penetration** — The distance a weld extends from its face into a joint, exclusive of reinforcement.

**Lap Joint** — A joint type in which the nonbutting ends of one or more workpieces overlap approximately parallel to one another.

**Machine Welding** — A nonstandard term when used for mechanized welding.

**Manual Process** — An operation with the torch, gun, or electrode holder held and manipulated by hand. Accessory equipment, such as part motion devices and handheld filler material feeders may be used.

**Melting Rate** — The weight or length of electrode, wire, rod, powder melted in a unit of time.

**Open Circuit Voltage** — The voltage between the output terminals of the power source when no current is flowing to the torch or gun.

**Overhead Welding Position** — The welding position in which welding is performed from the underside of the joint.

**Overlap** — The protrusion of weld metal beyond the weld toe or weld root.

**Peening** — The mechanical working of metals used impact blows.

**Porosity** — Cavity-type discontinuities formed by gas entrapment during solidification or in a thermal spray deposit.

**Postheating** — The application of heat to an assembly after welding, brazing, soldering, thermal spraying or thermal cutting operation.

**Preheat** — The heat applied to the base metal or substrate to attain and maintain preheat temperature.

**Radiography** — The use of radiant energy in the form of X-rays or gamma rays for the non-destructive examination of metals.

**Reverse Polarity** — A nonstandard term for direct current electrode positive.

**Root Opening** — A separation at the joint root between the workpieces.

**Root Penetration** — The distance the weld metal extends into the joint root.

**Semiautomatic Process** — An operation performed manually with equipment controlling one or more of the process conditions.

**Shielded Metal Arc Welding (SMAW)** — An arc welding process with an arc between a covered electrode and the weld pool. The process is used with shielding from the decomposition of the electrode covering, without the application of pressure, and with filler metal from the electrode.

**Slag** — A nonmetallic product resulting from the mutual dissolution of flux and nonmetallic impurities in some welding and brazing processes.

**Spatter** — The metal particles expelled during fusion welding which do not form a part of the weld.

**Straight Polarity** — A nonstandard term for direct current electrode negative.

**Stress Relief Heat Treatment** — Uniform heating of a structure or a portion thereof to a sufficient temperature to relieve the major portion of the residual stresses, followed by uniform cooling.

**Stringer Bead** — A straight weld bead on the surface of a plate, with little or no side-to-side electrode movement.

**Tack Weld** — A weld made to hold parts of a weldment in proper alignment until the final welds are made.

**Throat of a Fillet Weld**

   **Theoretical Throat** — The distance from the beginning of the joint root perpendicular to the hypotenuse of the largest right triangle that can be inscribed within the cross section of a fillet weld. This dimension is based on the assumption that the root opening is equal to zero.

   **Actual Throat** — The shortest distance between the weld root and the face of a fillet weld.

   **Effective Throat** — The minimum distance minus any convexity between the weld root and the face of a fillet weld.

**Tungsten Electrode** — A non-filler metal electrode used in arc welding or cutting, made principally of tungsten.

**Underbead Crack** — A heat-affected zone crack in steel weldments arising from the occurrence of a crack-susceptible microstructure, residual or applied stress, and the presence of hydrogen.

**Undercut** — A groove melted into the base metal adjacent to the weld toe or the root of a weld and left unfilled by welding.

**Vertical Welding Position** — The welding position in which the weld axis, at the point of welding, is approximately vertical, and the weld face lies in an approximately vertical plane.

**Weave Bead** — A type of weld bead made with transverse osscillation.

**Weld** – A localized coalescence of metals or non-metals produced either by heating the materials to welding temperature, with or without the application of pressure, or by the application of pressure alone, and with or without the use of filler material.

**Weld Face** — The exposed surface of a weld on the side from which welding was done.

**Weld Metal** — That portion of a weld which has been melted during welding.

**Weld Nomenclature** —

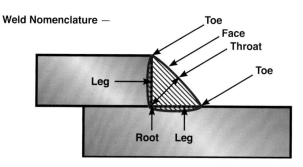

**Weld Pass** — A single progression of welding along a joint. The result of a pass is a weld bead or layer.

**Weld Pool** — The localized volume of molten metal in a weld prior to its solidification as weld metal.

**Weld Root** — The points, as shown in cross section, at which the root surface intersects the base metal and extends furthest into the weld joint.

**Weld Size**

    **Groove Weld Size** — The joint penetration of a groove weld.

    **Fillet Weld Size** — For equal leg fillet welds, the leg lengths of the largest isosceles right triangle that can be inscribed within the fillet weld cross section. For unequal leg fillet welds, the leg lengths of the largest right triangle that can be inscribed within the fillet weld cross section.

**Welding Procedure** — The detailed methods and practices involved in the production of a weldment.

**Weld Toe** — The junction of the weld face and the base metal.

**Welding Rod** — A form of welding filler metal, normally packaged in straight lengths, that does not conduct the welding current.

**Weldment** — An assembly joined by welding.

# Metric Conversion Tables

| To convert from | | To | Multiply by |
|---|---|---|---|
| lb | Mass (avdp) | kg | $4.535\,924 \times 10^{-1}$ |
| ton | Mass (200 lbm) | kg | $9.071\,847 \times 10^{2}$ |
| in | Linear Measurement | mm | $2.540\,000 \times 10$ |
| in$^2$ | Area Dimensions | mm$^2$ | $6.451\,600 \times 10^{2}$ |
| lb in.$^2$ | Pressure | Pa | $6.894\,757 \times 10^{3}$ |
| gal/hr | Flow Rate | liter/min | $6.309\,020 \times 10^{-2}$ |
| psi | Tensile Strength | Pa | $6.894\,757 \times 10^{3}$ |
| ksi. in.$^{1/2}$ | Fracture Toughness | MN m$^{-3/2}$ | $1.098\,855$ |
| ft. lb. | Impact | J | $1.355\,818$ |
| lb/hr | Deposition Rate | kg/h | $0.45$ |
| in/min | Travel/Wire Speed | mm/s | $4.233\,333 \times 10^{-1}$ |
| MPG | Miles per U.S. Gal. | km/liter | $0.425$ |
| MPG | Miles per Imp. Gal | km/liter | $0.3544$ |
| F$^\circ$ | Temperature | C$^\circ$ | $5/9 \times (F^\circ - 32^\circ)$ |
| C$^\circ$ | Temperature | F$^\circ$ | $9/5 \times C^\circ + 32^\circ$ |

| Fillet Sizes | |
|---|---|
| in. | mm |
| 1/8 | 3 |
| 5/32 | 4 |
| 3/16 | 5 |
| 1/4 | 6 |
| 5/16 | 8 |
| 3/8 | 10 |
| 7/16 | 11 |
| 1/2 | 13 |
| 5/8 | 16 |
| 3/4 | 19 |
| 7/8 | 22 |
| 1 | 25 |

| Electrode Sizes | |
|---|---|
| in. | mm |
| 0.030 | 0.8 |
| 0.035 | 0.9 |
| 0.040 | 1.0 |
| 0.045 | 1.2 |
| 1/16 | 1.6 |
| 5/64 | 2.0 |
| 3/32 | 2.4 |
| 1/8 | 3.2 |
| 5/32 | 4.0 |
| 3/16 | 4.8 |
| 1/4 | 6.4 |

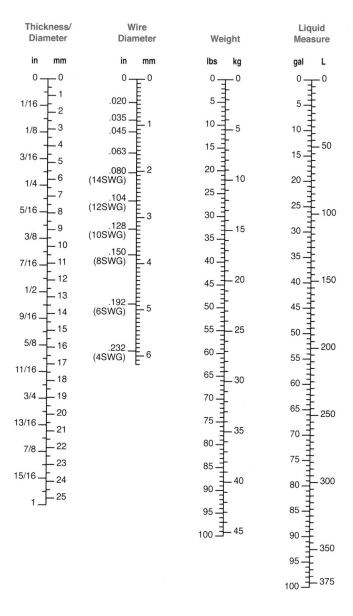

| Thickness/<br>Diameter | | Wire<br>Diameter | | Weight | | Liquid<br>Measure | |
|---|---|---|---|---|---|---|---|
| in | mm | in | mm | lbs | kg | gal | L |

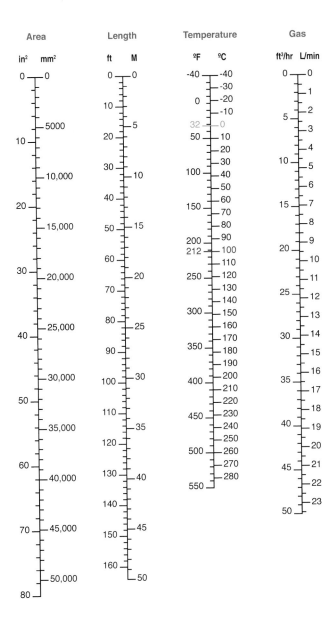

| Area | | Length | | Temperature | | Gas | |
|---|---|---|---|---|---|---|---|
| in² | mm² | ft | M | ºF | ºC | ft³/hr | L/min |

**Area**

in² — mm²
- 0 — 0
- — 5000
- 10 — 10,000
- 20 — 15,000
- 30 — 20,000
- — 25,000
- 40 — 30,000
- 50 — 35,000
- 60 — 40,000
- 70 — 45,000
- — 50,000
- 80

**Length**

ft — M
- 0 — 0
- 10 — 5
- 20
- 30 — 10
- 40
- 50 — 15
- 60
- 70 — 20
- 80 — 25
- 90
- 100 — 30
- 110
- 120 — 35
- 130 — 40
- 140
- 150 — 45
- 160
- — 50

**Temperature**

ºF — ºC
- -40 — -40
- — -30
- 0 — -20
- — -10
- 32 — 0
- 50 — 10
- — 20
- — 30
- 100 — 40
- — 50
- 150 — 60
- — 70
- — 80
- — 90
- 200 — 100
- 212 — 110
- 250 — 120
- — 130
- — 140
- 300 — 150
- — 160
- — 170
- 350 — 180
- — 190
- 400 — 200
- — 210
- — 220
- 450 — 230
- — 240
- — 250
- 500 — 260
- — 270
- — 280
- 550

**Gas**

ft³/hr — L/min
- 0 — 0
- — 1
- — 2
- 5 — 3
- — 4
- 10 — 5
- — 6
- 15 — 7
- — 8
- — 9
- 20 — 10
- — 11
- 25 — 12
- — 13
- 30 — 14
- — 15
- — 16
- 35 — 17
- — 18
- 40 — 19
- — 20
- 45 — 21
- — 22
- — 23
- 50

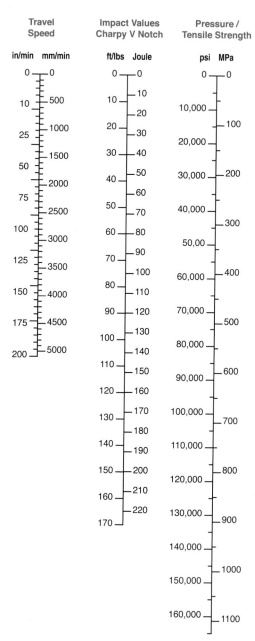

# HIWT Training and Certification Services

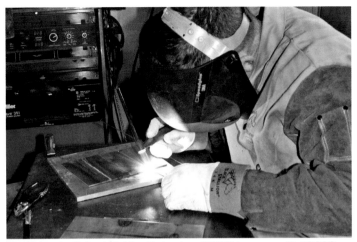

The Hobart Institute of Welding Technology (HIWT) is a nonprofit, ACCSC accredited institution dedicated to excellence in welding training and education. Founded in 1930, HIWT has trained over 85,000 men and women worldwide.

### Field & Specialized Training
HIWT offers field training (at your facility) & specialized training (at our facility) to make your welders more productive and profitable. Each program is custom designed to get your people up to speed in the shortest possible time.

### Complete Welding Skill Training Programs
Looking for an exciting career that pays well and is in high demand? Consider our 36-week Combination Structural & Pipe Welding Program or our 21-week Structural Welding Program. A variety of financial aid options are available for those who qualify. Individual skill classes are also available for hobbyists or individuals who want to upgrade their welding skills.

### Technical Training
Our preparation course for the AWS CWI/CWE Examination Is one of the best in the country. Hobart Institute also offers a 1-week course for Welding Instructors, as well as courses in welding inspection, quality control, NDT and weldability.

### Qualification & Certification Services
HIWT qualifies welding procedures and welders to structural, pressure piping, production and aerospace specifications on all types of ferrous and nonferrous materials.

For more information and a free catalog, visit us at **www.welding.org**, or contact us at: Hobart Institute of Welding Technology, 400 Trade Square East, Troy, OH 45373
Phone: (800) 332-9448 or (937) 332-9500 • Fax: (937) 332-9550

# HIWT Training Materials

**Put over 80 years of world-class welding training experience from the Hobart Institute of Welding Technology to work for you.**

- Complete "turn-key" curriculum materials on all major welding processes — entry-level through advanced (plate & pipe).

- Modular Design.

- Close-up shots of the welding arc highlighting proper technique.

- Easy-to-follow "how-to" student workbook design with "recipes" to help students recreate each weld, and summaries of essential theory.

- Based on AWS S.E.N.S.E. objectives, with standard AWS terms and definitions used throughout.

- Comprehensive Instructor Guides.

- Technical Guides on SMAW, GMAW, FCAW & GTAW.

- Programmed Learning Courses on Welding Symbols, Blueprint Reading, Pipe Layout, and Symbols for Nondestructive Examination.

- Wall posters.

- Plus a variety of useful welding texts from other publishers.

For more information, visit us at **www.welding.org**,
or call (800) 332-9448 Ext. 9509 • (937) 332-9551
for a free catalog.

# Index

# Index